THE Joan Collins BEAUTY BOOK

THE Joan Collins BEAUTY BOOK

M

This book is dedicated to
the memory of my mother Elsa,
who guided me in the right direction . . .

. . . and to the beauties of tomorrow:
Anoushka, Cassandra, Claire Louise,
Deborah, Emma, Genna, Georgina, Jade,
Jasmine, Kimberly, Lisa, Melissa,
Milica, Natasha, Polly, Rachel,
Romla, Rory, Samantha, Scheherazade,
Tiffany, Tracy, Victoria
and especially Tara and Katyana

Design by Robert Updegraff
Drawings by Jenny Powell
Copyright © Joan Collins 1980

First published 1980 by
Macmillan London Limited
London and Basingstoke

Reprinted 1981

Paperback edition published 1981

Associated companies in Auckland, Dallas,
Delhi, Dublin, Hong Kong, Johannesburg,
Lagos, Manzini, Melbourne, Nairobi,
New York, Singapore, Tokyo, Washington
and Zaria

Printed in Hong Kong

British Library Cataloguing in Publications Data

Collins, Joan

    The Joan Collins' beauty book.
    1, Beauty culture
    646.7'2   TT957
    ISBN 0-333-32608-3

Contents

Introduction

When today's woman thinks about beauty care, what she wants is to look as good as she can within her own physical framework, and to feel at the peak of her health and fitness and energy all the time. Modern beauty care is closely related to health, diet, exercise and lifestyle.

The Eighties are here, and with it women have new confidence and a self-awareness which has been building throughout the past decades. Our time is precious, and there is much to do and achieve in today's confused and hectic world. Modern woman is individual, active, self-confident and *real*. She knows who she is, what her aims in life are and how she wants to look. Even if she isn't quite sure, she is making a genuine effort to reach out and get there, whether by improving her mind, or by taking care of her face and body in the best way she knows.

Unfortunately there is a widely held attitude that any woman who wants to look her most attractive needs to spend hours a week on complicated beauty treatments and therapies, sleep nine or ten hours each night and spend a fortune on clothes. I have always felt that this is nonsense and a total waste of the valuable time that the modern woman just does not have to spare.

Of course there is a certain element of vanity involved in caring for yourself, but not only does an attractive appearance please the beholder, it also gives *you* a feeling of confidence and wellbeing and inner satisfaction. I always feel more confident when I know I look good than when I have thrown on any old thing and not bothered to do anything to my face or hair.

But obsession with beauty and with the so-called retention of youth is too time-consuming and narcissistic to be palatable or practical to me. I live my life as fully as possible: I pay attention to the upkeep of my health and looks, but not to the detriment of my enjoyment of life, and this includes eating well, drinking wine, staying up late, sunbathing and even, God forbid, smoking!

As an actress I have had to understand my looks, and what makes me tick in terms of make-up, clothes, diet, and life. I have staggered exhaustedly on to the film set at 7.30 in the morning, coiffed and cosmeticized to the nines to face hours in front of the relentless eyes of the camera (which never lies), having been up with a sick child all night and wishing only to curl up and sleep all day. I have always had to put my best face forward in my job, knowing it is part of my stock in trade, and that I am expected by most people with whom I come in contact to look in top form.

It is not just a question of paying attention to my beauty routine, it is also taking great care of my health. Health is every individual's greatest responsibility, because the daily living habits we choose are the main factor in how well we function. Some of us are born healthier than others, just as some are born better looking than others, but most of us have the potential to be healthier and more attractive than we are.

I have now devised a regime for myself that I think is intelligent without being obsessive, and healthful without being fanatical. And it works! It involves a certain amount of basic discipline which soon becomes second nature. I believe it is the key to a healthy, individual and attractive way of life and one in which 'age cannot wither her'. Health and vitality are divine gifts which we should fully appreciate and enjoy for as long as we can, and that means taking care of ourselves in the best way we can.

These are the principles – sensible and applicable to most women – which I have applied to myself since I was a teenager and which, with a little effort, any woman can apply to herself with beneficial results.

My long career in films, TV and the theatre has given me the marvellous opportunity of learning about all aspects of beauty and health by observation, trial and error, and interaction with other people. The information in this book is the result: the ideas, advice and tricks of the trade that will prove practical and helpful to all women. I look forward to sharing it with you.

Joan Collins

Lifestyle

The single most destructive factor in our emotional and mental lives today is stress. Our nerves and senses are constantly assailed by a barrage of tension-causing outside stimuli.

The noise level in today's society is reaching an almost intolerable level. Close your eyes now and unless you live deep in the heart of the country or are double glazed within an inch of your life, the amount of different sounds around you is quite amazing. Sitting in my bedroom right now in London I can hear the following: the radio in the kitchen, the phone ringing, a drill thumping away down the road, cars screeching their brakes and accelerating, and there goes the door bell again – it's an endless assault on the senses and on concentration.

Many of the diseases of today from which we suffer are caused by stress. Heart disease, insomnia, nervous breakdowns and disorders, skin diseases, stomach ailments – a long list of disorders brought on by modern living.

As an example of how stress can affect one's health and wellbeing, I will tell a personal story. A couple of years ago I was involved in a situation which was causing me intense grief. Because I am mentally quite strong, I did not crack up, nor did I have a nervous breakdown or commit suicide – all of which, at one time or the other, I felt

I was coming close to. I went about my life and work as normally as possible. Only my family and very close friends knew that I was actually under enormous strain and suffering a great deal.

But the stress and pain evinced itself in my skin. Having had a good, healthy, more or less blemish-free complexion all my life, I suddenly developed spots! Not just one or two but dozens and dozens of the little monsters appeared on my face and neck almost overnight. This would be bad enough for anyone, but for an actress it was a catastrophe.

After trying all my own remedies to no avail, I finally saw a dermatologist. He examined my skin and questioned me thoroughly. He then informed me that I was suffering from a common skin condition called roseola nervosa, which I translated into 'nervous acne'.

There was nothing I could do, said the doctor. The condition of my skin would clear up when my personal situation was resolved. Since the latter did not seem likely in the foreseeable future, I resigned myself to months of disfigurement. Eventually, as predicted, when my problem sorted itself out so my skin started to clear up, and luckily today my complexion is much the same as it was before.

Good health is of course more than the absence of any apparent disease. Many people think that because they have no obvious symptoms or illness, they are healthy. They ignore the fact that they might be potentially ill through bad dietary habits, too much smoking, lack of exercise, and extreme stress and tension. Because our bodies are capable of adapting to these stresses and strains, at least for the first thirty or forty years of our lives, we are often not aware of impending disease until the symptoms manifest themselves outwardly. Illness begins in the body weeks, months, even years before you actually feel ill. And the seeds of this illness are usually planted by lack of care and attention to what we do with our bodies from the day we are born.

Many doctors still scoff at this. They would rather prescribe a pill or an antibiotic than trace the root of the problem. But prevention is better than cure, and that is why you should see your body as a finely tuned, complicated, sophisticated machine, which must be cherished and nourished with as much care as you would your newborn baby.

You may ask what you can do to eliminate potential problems and reduce or banish stress from your life. It is not easy, but examining and understanding the causes and then making a gradual change in your lifestyle can alleviate tension and may help a great deal.

Relaxation

Try to become aware of muscle tension in everyday activities and then to reduce it. As you go about your daily tasks learn to isolate the areas of tension you feel in particular parts of your body and concentrate on relaxing them. After a while you can do this automatically. For example if you have pain in the lower back, you are probably unconsciously tensing your lower back muscles when you are in a stressful situation – and by this I mean any of the petty day-to-day aggravations of modern life such as being shoved in the bus queue, jostled in the underground, fuming in traffic jams, and so on.

Once a day make time to sit in a chair or lie on a bed quietly and let yourself unwind. Take a deep breath. Close your eyes and try to identify the parts of your body that seem tense. Is it your back? Your neck? Your stomach? We all have different places in our bodies where tension builds up. When you have found the tension areas you must concentrate on relaxing them, and once you have done this you will feel the relaxation spreading and your whole body will begin to feel more at ease.

You may have to work hard to learn the art of relaxation, for it is indeed an art, but it will pay off in terms of mental and physical health.

Here are some complete relaxing techniques

Choose a quiet, calm environment with as few distractions as possible. This will contribute to the effectiveness of the relaxation by making it easier for you to concentrate.

Choose a comfortable position so that there is no undue muscular tension. The easiest is a sitting position: if you are lying down there is a tendency to fall asleep. Although many people have reported that they use this relaxation exercise while lying in bed to help them go to sleep, if you fall asleep using the technique you are not experiencing genuine relaxation, which is quite different from sleep.

Close your eyes.

Begin to relax all your muscles, beginning at your feet and working up to your head; mentally hold the idea of each part of your body relaxing.

Breathe through your nose. Begin to become aware of your breathing and as you are breathing out say the word 'relax', silently to yourself. Breathe in . . . breathe out, 'relax'; breathe in . . . out, 'relax', and so on. While you are doing the exercise breathe easily and naturally. This device of repeating silently a word or phrase helps to break the train of distracting thoughts and allows the body and mind to relax.

Continue this process for 10–20 minutes. If your mind begins to wander, focus your attention back on the repetition of the word 'relax'. Try not to worry about how well you are performing the technique because this in itself will prevent true relaxation. Adopt a passive, 'let it happen' attitude.

I was taught this technique for relaxing by Dr Robert Giller of New York. I use it whenever I am in a particularly stressful period – which is quite often, I regret to say – and it definitely works for me.

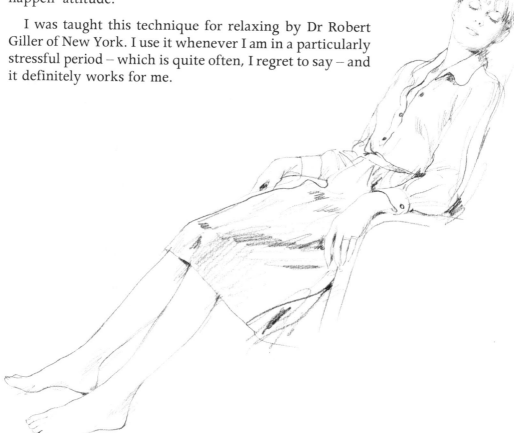

Sleep

Just being asleep is often not as restful as it seems. How many times do you wake in the night? Does your partner disturb you by snoring or tossing and turning? Do the children come down for a drink of water? Does the baby wake up? You would be surprised if you counted up in actual hours how much deep sleep you have had, how much has really been beneficial. If you haven't had at least $6\frac{1}{2}$–$7\frac{1}{2}$ hours a night, try to get half an hour's nap or lie down during the day.

Sleep is nature's oldest and most trusted beauty treatment. Some of the legendary beauties of yesterday who still look good swear that they owe their looks and beauty to 12 or 14 hours' sleep a night! I myself think this is a waste of productive time which could be better spent doing many more interesting and valuable things.

You spend about one-third of your adult lifetime asleep, but what else other than rest do you get out of it? All your internal organs get a chance to rest and restore themselves. In the morning your stomach is flatter, because all food has been thoroughly digested. Any tension that may have accumulated during the previous day will usually have disappeared. Your batteries have been recharged and your cells revitalized, which is why after a good night's sleep your eyes have more sparkle and your skin more of a glow.

As we get older we need less sleep. If you couldn't exist on less than 9 hours a night aged twenty you may find that at thirty you feel fine with 7 or 8, and at forty you can get by with 6 hours. There are some lucky people who actually only need 1 or 2 hours' sleep a night and function perfectly on that. Think of all those extra hours of productivity or leisure one would have.

Sometimes you may need 8 hours a night and drop off as soon as your head hits the pillow, and sometimes you lie there unable to sleep, restless and frustrated until the early hours. This is really perfectly natural. Sometimes you need to eat a lot in one day and sometimes you don't feel hungry at all. Your body's metabolism is different at different times of the month or year. So don't fight it. Your body knows best. Read a book, have a hot scented bath or a glass of warm milk, and give up trying to force sleep on yourself. The more uptight and angry you become, the harder it will be to rest.

One night's lack of sleep or a small amount of sleep will not have a devastatingly dreadful effect on your body or looks. Try to catch up the next night. As far as amounts of sleep go, let your body judge how much you need.

Diet

Whatever sort of pressure you live under, tucking a healthy breakfast under your belt in the morning can do a lot to alleviate it. There is something to be said for the slogan 'Eat breakfast like a king, lunch like a lord and dinner like a pauper'. Going to work on a cup of coffee and a saccharin tablet, although it may be good for the waistline, is not in the long run beneficial to the stress factor, which seems to be part of most people's lives today. Allow yourself plenty of time to have breakfast quietly; this will put you in a calm mood to face any problems that the day may bring. Being late or in a rush creates tension which may last all day.

Breakfast is important because there is likely to have been a gap of 8–14 hours since your previous meal. Your blood sugar needs raising, and your energy level must be revved up. Therefore some protein (e.g. eggs, cottage cheese), some carbohydrates (toast – wholewheat, please!) and some natural sugar (orange juice, grapefruit or honey) should be part of your normal breakfast. (There are more suggestions for breakfast on pages 48–9.)

If you do skip breakfast, you will suffer for it. It is much better to give lunch a miss occasionally and take a walk in the park than to leave out that all-important breakfast. Even when I have to get up at 5.30am to go to the studio I always have either a glass of orange juice or some tea with honey before I leave. (Those lucky actors whose call is before 7am get served a full breakfast in the make-up chair.)

I shall stress many times in this book the utter necessity of correct nutrition and diet. Let me emphasize one thing here, however.

What you *don't* eat is just as important as what you *do*. Try to eliminate or at least cut down the following:
Processed and over-refined foods
Foods full of chemical additives, such as hot dogs, bacon, soft drinks
Pre-cooked, packaged, fabricated, pseudo-foods
Foods high in animal fat and cholesterol.

Cut out unnecessary consumption of stimulants and irritants. These contribute towards stress, and although they are sometimes unavoidable they should be taken as seldom as possible. They include coffee, tea, alcohol, fizzy drinks, salt, tap water, aspirins and anti-histamines. (If the inclusion of tap water in this list surprises you, turn to page 43.)

Exercise

The importance of adequate exercise is covered fully in Chapter 2, but let me repeat and underline that exercise is *essential* for eliminating the effects of a stressful life and giving you the physical wellbeing and confidence that leads to true beauty.

Sex

Spending time on sex or beauty makes many people feel vaguely guilty. But sex is one of the best and cheapest of all beauty treatments. So get over the guilt and enjoy it.

Real beauty comes from confidence and from being in touch with your own body. It is natural, not narcissistic, to like and enjoy your body, and any movement that gives you sensual pleasure helps to increase your awareness of yourself. Dancing, swimming, stretching, running – all of these give us the opportunity to be in touch with our own physicality. And only by appreciating our own bodies can we really enjoy other people's.

This does not mean that you have to strive for the perfect physical ripeness of cover girls and models – such perfection remains the prerogative of only a few. But you must realize that your body is beautiful in its own way : it is unique and individual, just as you are. To feel self-conscious in sex because of what you think are physical flaws is a sure way to sow the seeds of unease and embarrassment that will negate what should be a fulfilling experience.

A healthy sex life that gives you pleasure is an important part of feeling and looking great. It's an old cliché but true, that sex makes your skin glow and your eyes sparkle. It also makes you less edgy and nervous. And one of the greatest beauty treatments in the world is being in love – by which I mean the state of total euphoria that comes in the early stages of a romance or involvement. (There is also an unusual lack of appetite which is great for the figure!)

New romance is wonderful and spine-tingling and thrilling, but old romance is good too – and a happy marriage better still. In fact any kind of emotion that involves total care and commitment to another human being, be it baby or boyfriend, is beneficial to your looks.

Smoking and alcohol

The danger of smoking has been rammed down our throats a zillion times, and it's now a proven fact. So try to cut down even if you can't kick the habit. Each cigarette is like the bullet in a gun playing a game of Russian roulette: you never know which one could trigger off a dormant disease in your body.

Smoking is supposed to encourage the formation of wrinkles and although there is no proof of this, it is a fact that each cigarette uses up 25mg of Vitamin C in your body. Anyone who smokes heavily is almost certain to be short of this important vitamin and should take extra Vitamin C.

What smoking definitely does is contribute to lung cancer. Now that more women are smoking, many more incidents of lung cancer are being found in women. People who smoke are also more susceptible to heart palpitations, coughs, colds and respiratory conditions such as emphysema, and influenza. Nicotine is a potent drug which affects every cell in your body; it also dulls the hair and skin.

Alcohol not only uses up the B vitamins (see p. 41) which play a major role in beauty but it also encourages the appearance of threadlike veins on cheeks and nose which are almost impossible to eradicate and very ugly. If you like drinking, drink wine. A wine spritzer (with soda or mineral water and ice) is even better. Whisky, gin and vodka are particularly bad for the thread-vein condition.

Drugs

Finally, my particular *bête noire* and what I (and many doctors) now consider to be one of the most totally destructive substances we can put into our bodies.

So-called soft drugs such as marijuana (pot or grass) and hashish are just as detrimental to your health in the long term as the hard drugs (cocaine and heroin). The taking of drugs has become almost socially acceptable in some quarters today and although marijuana is now legal in America, it does not mean that the cumulative effects are not really bad for you – after all cigarettes are also legal and we are all aware how dangerous they can be.

It has now been proven that smoking marijuana destroys brain cells, impairs the ability of the body to function properly, slows down bodily reactions, decreases sex drive (although initially it may increase it), changes body metabolism, makes it difficult to concentrate and finally *is* addictive (in spite of what the 'experts' say). For young people and teenagers it can destroy their lives. As far as looks go for women it is nothing less than disastrous. It causes premature wrinkling of the facial skin, a dull muddy complexion, bloodshot yellowing eyes and lack-lustre hair.

The other insidious thing about smoking marijuana or hashish is that it often results in experimentation with hard drugs such as cocaine and heroin. I reluctantly sniffed some cocaine in St Tropez about twelve years ago when the 'jet set' were considering it the new chic thing to do. I couldn't sleep for 48 hours, and had a sore throat and post nasal drip for three weeks. Needless to say I haven't gone near it since. As for heroin it is one of the most utterly destructive things to a human being, mentally, physically and emotionally. Eventually those who snort it will inject, and that is the beginning of the end. It is unbelievably addictive, causing people to become almost zombies if they don't take it, and they begin to *need* it to function even half properly.

So my advice is to keep clear of all drugs, or if you've got the habit – break it before it breaks you.

Body Care
and Exercise

Standards of feminine beauty change radically over the centuries, and if you look at a portrait of a great beauty from the sixteenth, seventeenth or eighteenth century it is hard to believe that she would rate a second glance in the High Street today.

We are taller, slimmer and more muscular than the women of previous generations. The average height of a Western woman today is 5ft 4in. One hundred years ago it was 5ft 1in. What will it be by the year 2080?

Looking at the pictures and drawings that follow, you will see what an amazing difference in body structure has evolved during the twentieth century.

1900–1914

An hour-glass figure was the ideal. Women wore whale-bone, satin and cambric corsets that squeezed their mid-section into an actual 'S' shape. An 18-inch waist was the goal. If you weighed fourteen stone it was not an easy task, but the relentless corset squeezed in all spare flesh to suffocation point. Internal organs were constricted, and ladies were constantly getting the vapours due to their circulation being cut off and preventing the flow of blood to the brain. These corsets pushed their bosoms up to form an ample shelf. On top of the corset, at the back, a bustle was worn to accentuate the hour-glass shape, and over everything was an inexplicable amount of knickers, bloomers, vests and petticoats absolutely larded with lace. It was a miracle that they could move, let alone breathe.

This look gave women a totally artificial body shape, and it is incredible that the fashion lasted for so many years since it must have been quite agonizing to wear.

1914–1920

With the advent of the First World War, women were forced into carrying out more of the tasks previously done by men. They started working in factories and shops, hospitals, buses and trains.

It was the first time that a war had involved women so actively, and naturally the 'S' shaped hour-glass figure became obsolete as it impaired physical movement. The

The wildly exaggerated curves of the hour-glass figure fashionable at the beginning of the century (below, left) had swung by the Twenties to an equally artificial opposite – the flat-chested tubular look shown below.

tight corset gave way to a more relaxed silhouette. It was still firmly corseted, but the waist was not as cinched and the bust not pushed up to look like a pouter pigeon. Women started to be actively involved in sports towards the end of the second decade, and 'sports costumes' came into fashion.

The Twenties

The Twenties saw the emergence of the first emancipated woman. Emancipated she may have been, but underneath her loosely flowing short frock, daringly revealing more leg than had ever been seen before, was a firm canvas corset which started at the breastbone and ended at the thigh. It compressed the body into complete flatness, obliterating any sign of a bosom or waist. Most women wore this contraption, with the exception of a few lucky young 'flappers' who were youthful, daring and firm-fleshed enough to wear *nothing* underneath their dresses, to the outrage of society. This was a time in which boobs were out – if you were flat-chested you were the ideal.

The Thirties

The Roaring Twenties waned. The world went into a depression. The bosom started to be emphasized again but most women still wore a full one-piece corset. By now it had a light boning to accentuate the waist and bust, with suspenders attached to keep up the stockings. At night sexy bias-cut evening dresses revealed more of what was uncorseted underneath, and many women, copying movie stars such as Jean Harlow and Joan Crawford, wore no underwear at all. During the Thirties the body shape, through the fashion of the day, became much more natural. This meant a return of the waistline, with corsets having inserts of satin or fabric to give a slightly waisted look.

1940–1947

Again we were at war – this time wearing trousers and masculine clothes. The body shape was still disguised by padded shoulders and intricate detail and draping on clothes. Women wore 'roll-ons', elastic girdles with suspenders that held in their stomachs and hips. They also wore very *seriously* constructed brassières. Howard Hughes invented the 'uplift' bra for Jane Russell, and some bosoms looked like up-ended ice cream cones that grew from beside the armpits!

1947

Christian Dior launched his 'new look' to a furore of publicity, and women were back in corsets once more – what a regression. The silhouette was again wasp-waisted, busty and hippy, and to achieve it women wore girdles, an uplift bra for the fashionable pointed bosom and a 'waist cincher' which gave them a 21-inch waist, come what may. Skirts were long and cumbersome, and fashionable women looked like stiff dolls.

The Mid-Fifties

The cinched waist and structured look stayed until the Fifties when the 'sack' dress evolved. Instantly every woman threw away her girdle, waist cincher and corset, with a gasp of relief. Now there was a total de-emphasizing of the body, and as clothes became looser and more relaxed so did foundation garments and attitudes in general.

The more relaxed look of the early Forties which resulted from woman's role in the Second World War did not last long: by 1947 the 'new look' introduced by Dior had women back in corsets again, as restricted as they were in Victorian times.

The Sixties

This was the most radically changing of all the decades. Skirts zoomed to the thigh. Dresses were cut out in oddly original places all over the body – back, midriff and arms. More flesh was exposed. More and more bodies needed to look good. The look was young, fun and cute, and to go with it came tights, lightweight unboned bras and bikini pants. Goodbye for ever, we hoped, to stockings and suspender belts, boned bras and waist cinchers, corsets and girdles.

Body studios and gyms started up in earnest in the Sixties. With such an emphasis on youthful looks and with the short skirts showing so much leg and thigh, women started to be aware that they had to keep their bodies toned and in perfect shape; they couldn't depend on foundation garments any more.

The tailored look of the Sixties no longer depended on foundation garments but on a genuine good body shape. Trouser suits caught on in a big way, though few of them were as overtly masculine as the one I am wearing here, which is why I have put a veil with it.

The Seventies

In the Seventies as far as fashion went – anything went. Long full skirts, short tight skirts, jeans, trousers, the peasant look, the tailored look, the tarty look, the ethnic look. Each look came and went and sometimes lingered. What is obvious though is that with skin-tight jeans, skirts and sweaters, see-through blouses and shirts and short shorts, clinging jersey and wool dresses, it is impossible to look good without the best foundation that money *can't* buy – a great body.

It is every woman's right and aim, and it is the key to looking and feeling in top physical condition.

With the advent of the Seventies all constraints on the body were removed and a minimum of underwear was needed – just a well-toned firm body.

Why exercise?

One of the reasons why we need a perfectly toned body today more than ever is that we can no longer rely on structured undergarments to give us the shape we want.

Exercise does not work miracles, however. Contrary to popular opinion you do not lose much weight from it, unless it is very heavy physical exercise. What exercise *does* do for you is the following:

Firms up your flesh in all the right places.
Delays the ageing process considerably.
Improves digestion and coordination of movement, and counteracts insomnia and stress.
Makes you more supple and thus more graceful, and radically improves posture.
Strengthens the heart. The heart is a muscle, the most important muscle in the body, and muscles that are not used get weaker. Exercise also increases circulation.
Makes joints more flexible; lack of exercise causes the joints to deteriorate.
Has a calming effect on the nerves.
Makes kidneys function better.
Could put years on your life if you do it regularly.
Gives you a tremendous feeling of wellbeing and a glow.

Did you know that if you start a programme of exercises between the ages of thirty and forty, and do them religiously half an hour a day or $3\frac{1}{2}$ hours a week, or twice a week for $1\frac{1}{2}$ hours, your body will remain virtually the same (with the additional benefits of the exercise, of course) until you are well into your fifties and sixties? This means that if you start exercising weighing 16 stone you shouldn't expect to become 12 stone in a month, but if for example you are in moderately good shape at thirty-five, weighing more or less what is right for your height and age-group, you can expect to maintain this with hardly any change over the next two or three decades.

Look at that supreme example of a beautiful woman over fifty-five, Dame Margot Fonteyn. She is a living testament to the fact that using your body regularly keeps it from disintegrating into middle-aged spread and all the other nasties that so often start to accumulate over the age of thirty-five.

Keeping fit

Look at some six month old or six year old children. See how they never stop moving. Each and every muscle and sinew in their tiny bodies is constantly employed. The six month old is experimenting – starting to use and build the muscles that should last a lifetime. Alas this isn't always so. As they progress into adulthood the way they use their bodies starts to change, and they move and exercise less and less. My eight year old is never still. Even in front of the television she is moving, pushing her legs up and down, turning over on her tummy, stretching each and every part of herself. She never walks if she can run, she never sits if she can stand and jig about a bit – usually on one leg.

Compare this with the average twenty-five year old. 'Walk? What not me, I'm going in a bloody taxi' – or a bus, or a tube, or a car – as Eliza Doolittle would have said. At the department store the adults are queuing to use the lifts for one or two floors – it's the teenagers who zestily climb the stairs two or three at a time, their bodies filled with the vigour and vitality that starts evaporating in the mid-twenties and thirties, until by the forties the average man or woman is hard pressed to climb two flights of stairs without huffing and puffing like an aged dinosaur.

And why? Because they're plain out of practice at the simple and old-fashioned method of physical activity. A game of golf or tennis once a week maybe, a walk to the pub or the shops, and of course two weeks of summer hols lounging about in a deck chair – but hardly anybody, with the exception of heavy manual labourers, does *nearly* enough natural bodily exercise. Look at that fifty year old woman, look at her muscle tone. What muscle tone? Look at the loose flab allowed to accumulate on what must have once been a reasonably lithe and attractive frame.

The majority of children and teenagers are lithe and attractive. Just pop down to your local disco and take a look at them gyrating, those tight little bottoms in figure-hugging jeans. They may not all look like John Travolta or Bo Derek but they're energetic and fit, they're in shape and they're *young*. Now go down to the local pub or supermarket and see them twenty years later – flab, cellulite, floppy thighs and stomach, and a general look of sloppiness. Why? Their bodies have not been used for ages, and as with any piece of fine machinery, the less they are used, the more they will atrophy.

So here you are, anywhere between twenty-five and fifty, and your body has turned into a mechanism you just can't control. It's too late, you think; after all these years of abuse or non-use, how can this body be saved?

Well I say it is possible, depending on your desire and with a little bit of will power and discipline thrown in. A keep-fit regime, if stuck to for the rest of your life, can bring you energy, vitality and fitness you never knew you had. To achieve results you must train yourself to new permanent attitudes towards exercise. Physical fitness is just as important as good eating habits, and if the body is properly used, toned and cared for it has less difficulty in burning up food.

For me exercise is as necessary for survival as eating and drinking. When I don't exercise for a few days I feel sluggish and fat and my body starts losing its muscle tone.

When I am in London I go to a gym run by a gentleman called Dreas Reyneke, whose list of clients is impressive and includes many dancers and actors and actresses as well as solicitors, housewives and people from all walks of life. He uses a method based on centuries-old Oriental techniques, although most of the exercises are done on a machine called the Universal Body Reformer, invented by Dr Pilates some forty or fifty years ago. This technique is now being used in many gyms and health clubs throughout America and England. It works on a system of muscle resistance to springs, and involves dynamic tension and a form of Yoga, and lots of stretching. I have seen photographs of Dr Pilates taken in the 1930s when he was in his forties, and then again thirty years later when his body showed little change. It is quite amazing, and he owes it all to the UBR and regular exercising.

Obviously we cannot all have access to these machines, and neither can I all the time. Since I am often travelling I have adapted some of these exercises so that I can do them in a hotel room, my dressing room or anywhere where there is enough floor space. You can spend a minimum of time and still get maximum results.

I must stress here that no one should start a rigorous regime of exercise without first making sure that she is in reasonable health. If at the age of forty you suddenly decide to do all the exercises described below without

building up to them gradually, you could find yourself
with a strained back and aching muscles, having done more
than your body is capable of.

It will not be possible for those of you who have never
exercised to achieve the amount of repetition recommended
for most of these exercises, therefore I do advise a slow build-
up approach to each one, until eventually you reach the final
goal of feeling strong and fit enough to exercise strenuously
for 20–40 minutes a session.

*Bending and stretching
exercises are vital for
keeping your muscles supple
and strong: the exercise
may look difficult but it
can be achieved eventually
with practice.*

The stomach is one of the most vulnerable areas for gaining weight, particularly if you have had children. Lie on the floor on your right side, with your weight on your right elbow and your left knee drawn up to your stomach. Raise and straighten the leg as far as you can, and stretch your left hand towards your toes. Feel the muscles tense. Repeat this a dozen times, then change sides.

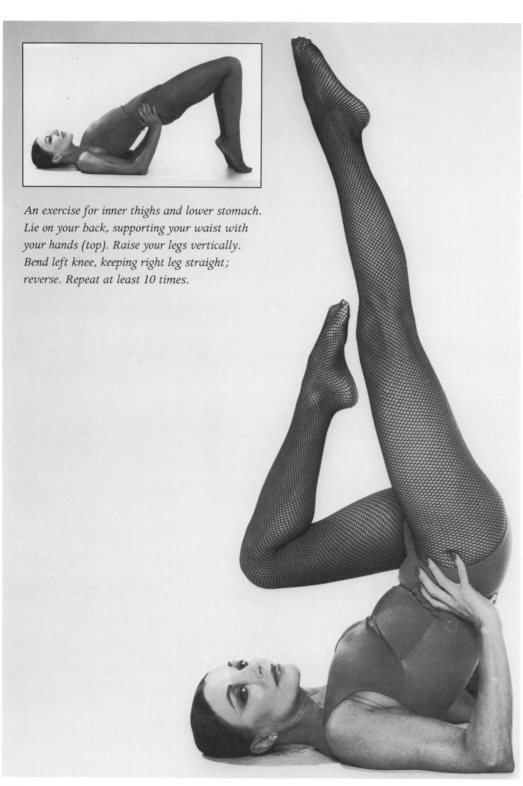

An exercise for inner thighs and lower stomach.
Lie on your back, supporting your waist with
your hands (top). Raise your legs vertically.
Bend left knee, keeping right leg straight;
reverse. Repeat at least 10 times.

This exercise kills three birds with one stone – waist, arms and inner thighs – though not everyone will be able to work up to the complete splits position. Sit on the floor with your legs apart, stretch from the waist with your arm as high as you can, keeping the body as taut as possible. Bend to the left with your arm arched, and then to the right.

Stomach Lie down, then sit up with your legs and arms extended, keeping them as taut as possible and angled to the left, with your toes outstretched. Hold for a second and then lie down again. Repeat, angling the arms and legs to the right.

Breasts have no muscle tissue, so it is important to keep the chest muscles which support them firmed up. This exercise of pressing the palms tightly together over your head for two seconds, then relaxing, should be done regularly.

Inner thighs and waist *Lie on the floor on your left side, with your left elbow supporting the body. Do not slump. Try to feel as much stretch in your waist as possible. Raise your right leg as far as it will go, keeping it very straight and keeping all you muscles tensed. Do this at least 12 times each side. When you are more advanced 2lb weights can be strapped on to each ankle.*

Stomach *A particularly good exercise for beginners or after having a baby because it is not too strenuous. Lie flat on your back, arms folded behind the head. Raise your right leg off the ground and extend it as high as possible. Lower it slowly. Repeat alternately a minimum of 10 times. Make sure that the stomach muscles are pulled in and your lower back is flat against the floor.*

Upper arm *Stand straight, with your legs back and arms extended straight out on each side with the palms facing out. Rotate the palms in small* circles several times, clockwise and anticlockwise. *Make sure your arms are tense and stiff.*

Waist exercise *Stand with your legs apart, right arm gently arched over your head and left arm flat to the side of the body. Bend sideways from the waist to the left keeping the right arm still arched. Feel the pull in your waist. Do at least 15 times, working up to 30, and then repeat on the other side.*

A variation on the waist exercise on the left. Do the same except use both arms, keeping the fingers laced over your head. Bend alternately to the left and right.

The most relaxing room in our house is our bedroom. It is where I get away from everyday pressures, for when working I need to relax as much as possible. I spend a lot of time there reading, telephoning, writing, watching TV and naturally sleeping, so I try to make it as comfortable, attractive and practical as possible.

At Stobo Castle health spa. Here I am enjoying the benefits of fresh air, beautiful scenery and healthy exercise deep in the heart of Scotland.

Health spas

Not many women can afford to allow themselves the luxury of three or four days at a restful and luxurious health and beauty spa, where they may forget about the daily stress and strain of modern life and be pampered mentally and physically. With a little organization and ingenuity, however, it is possible to emulate the kind of beneficial beauty treatments and relaxing atmosphere that these places supply.

Let me tell you something about what a health spa can and does do for you. I have visited several in the past few years, not so much to lose weight as to take stock of my life – to relax and get away from exterior annoyances such as phones and doorbells ringing, unwanted visitors, and the general pressures of my profession. I have been to Inglewood, a beautiful old country house in Berkshire, to Buxted Park, which alas no longer exists, to Forest Mere and Grayshott Hall, all beautiful, comfortable and designed for maximum relaxation. But recently I went deep into the heart of Scotland, about an hour out of Edinburgh, and discovered the delights of a new health and beauty spa called Stobo Castle.

Set in the gently rolling hills of the Scottish Borders with a magnificent view of the river Tweed and the romantic Eildon Hills, the gorgeous 170 year old Georgian castle is as beautiful within as it is dramatic without. You feel at peace as soon as you enter the sumptuous surroundings, for the atmosphere is extremely relaxed and informal. On the morning of the first day a tray of tea and honey and a small bowl of fruit is brought to your room. Then, dressed in a terry cloth robe provided by the spa, you go for your figure diagnosis. Weight and measurements are taken and a regime is suggested that will bring you the most benefits during your stay. The range of treatments is extensive, and unless you stay for a week it is impossible to fit everything in. As I had only three days to spare I chose three basic treatments: a steam cabinet, a massage with aromatic oils – very soothing and relaxing – and the exercise room, where I made use of the various machines available. I took a facial, a pedicure, a manicure and had my hair done. In three days I lost 5lb and came away feeling fit and ready to face the world again.

The home health spa

How can you achieve this without going to a spa? It is not easy, but with a little help from a friend who like you feels in need of a lift, here's how you could manage to turn your own home into a mini health spa for three days. If you live alone it is of course infinitely easier, and can be done at the weekend when you are not working. If you have a family some ingenuity is necessary, and the time must be taken while husband and children are at work and school, which should give you a good six or eight hours a day.

Do all the necessary shopping, cleaning, washing and ironing two days beforehand, get it out of the way and let it pile up while you're indulging yourself. To hell with housework! Make casseroles or large salads and store them in the fridge so that your husband and kids won't starve, and make them do the dishes for a change. (I realize that this isn't possible if you have small babies or toddlers, unless you can park them with parents or in-laws for a few days.) With your neighbour or a girl friend installed, start as soon as the family have left. Take the phone off the hook and put a note on the front door saying 'No visitors'.

Day One
Weigh yourselves and write down the results. Put on a comfortable old robe and run a hot bath, adding plenty of bubble bath or bath oil. Get out your face lotions and creams. Give yourself a simple facial, using a tablespoon of camomile leaves (available from health food shops) to a pint of boiling water. Tuck your hair away, place a towel over your head, and let the steam penetrate your pores for about five minutes. Pat dry then apply a face mask (see page 74). Leave it on for ten minutes, then wash off with tepid water.

Now for some exercises. First select the areas of your body that you feel most need reducing, and wrap them firmly with cling film or even a plastic garbage bag. Wind it around the stomach, for instance, as though you were bandaging yourself; you can do this everywhere except your bosom. The cling film causes you to sweat more freely in those places and thus burns off the fat quicker. Then put on a leotard or bathing suit, and spend one hour doing the exercises described on pages 20–29. You will find that doing these with your friend will give you more incentive to try harder, and a certain competitive spirit will emerge.

You can listen to the radio if you like – Radio 3 or 4 is more soothing than Top of the Pops.

It is now time for a very simple lunch: one apple and one orange or grapefruit, peeled, cored and served on your prettiest glass dish, with half a plain yoghurt. And plenty of water – you should drink at least three or four glasses, preferably mineral or bottled water, throughout the day.

After lunch lie down on a bed or sofa with a book or a magazine or watch TV. Try to sleep or doze or just relax for a couple of hours, shutting your mind to any mundane problems you might have. Try the relaxing technique described on pages 3–4. When you awake – refreshed and replenished, I hope – put conditioner all over your hair and rub it in thoroughly (you will leave this on overnight, covered with a scarf). Now give yourself a pedicure (see page 134). When your nails are dry have a cup of weak lemon tea with one spoonful of honey, and then spend half an hour on some relaxing Yoga exercises. Soon it will be time for the family to return, but instead of doing your usual housewifely duties, try to be as calm and relaxed as you can and do as little household work as possible.

To bed *early* – the same time as the children if possible, but try to get at least 9 to 10 hours' sleep. You may have tea with lemon and honey before retiring.

Day Two
Do exactly the same as on Day One, except this time have a manicure instead of a pedicure, and wash the conditioner off your hair and give yourself a shampoo and set.

Day Three
Follow the routine of the first two days, but take the time allocated for hair and nails to practise a super new make-up on your face, which by now should be positively glowing with rest and health! Pluck your eyebrows if necessary, and spend some time experimenting with different shades and colours of make-up and shadows and blushers. Put on your prettiest outfit, and when the family return you can join them in a proper tea or dinner (but go easy on the stodge). You should have lost at least 3–6lb and $\frac{1}{2}$–2 inches from waist, stomach and hips.

Of course there'll be a lot of housework piled up, but you will find you have plenty of energy and can whisk through the laundry, dishes and dusting in record time. You should feel and look terrific. If you don't, sue me!

While the family eat what you have prepared the previous night, you will eat your special diet salad:
 $\frac{1}{2}$ cup chopped celery
 $\frac{1}{2}$ cup chopped cucumber
 1 carrot, shredded
 $\frac{1}{2}$ tomato cut in small pieces
 3 or 4 pieces of raw cauliflower
 shredded onion (if you like it)
Make a dressing of lemon, vinegar, salt and pepper and a small amount of olive oil or sesame seed oil. If you are really hungry you may have 4oz cottage cheese, or 1oz Mozzarella cheese, or a hard-boiled egg with the salad. If you can't bear raw vegetables, make a similar salad with fruits – apple, orange, pear, melon and berries if in season.

Diet

You don't have to be rich to be beautiful. I've heard the old moan many times: 'It's easy for Jackie Kennedy (or Sophia Loren, or whoever is the latest Fabulous Over-Forty) to look good. She can *afford* the right kind of food or special exercise.' But the right kind of food needed to get your body in shape is considerably less expensive than the wrong kind of food, by which I mean pre-packaged, frozen, convenience foods extensively advertized on television that seem to form the bulk of the average person's intake. Two oranges are cheaper than a packet of biscuits, plus supplying much of the Vitamin C you need for a day.

A healthy day's food

Start with a glass of freshly squeezed orange juice.

Wholewheat or wholegrain bread is only slightly more expensive than white bread, which has about as much nutritional value as a slice of cardboard. Refined to the point of nutritional non-existence, it gives you nothing your body needs, merely staving off hunger pains, building calories and generating no energy.

Margarine is cheaper than butter and infinitely better for you because it is not animal fat. Butter, which is very heavy in cholesterol, is something you should try to cut out of your diet as much as possible.

Honey has more natural sweetness and more goodness than the supermarket jams, which are full of preservatives and artificial colouring.

So that's your breakfast, with a cup of tea or de-caffeinated coffee – and if you must have sugar, *don't* take the white kind. Again, it is totally useless nutritionally. Use honey, or if your sweet tooth cannot be soothed with anything else, take the heavy brown muscovado unrefined sugar. I don't believe in sweeteners such as saccharine and saxin: the fewer additives and foreign substances you take the better. These substances remain in the body for some time, and although it has not yet been proven what accumulative damage they may cause, I believe that any foreign substance in the body is eventually poisonous to the system.

Probably by around 11am you're feeling peckish and heading for the biscuits, doughnuts and a nice cup of coffee. Try instead a hard-boiled egg, a piece of cheese, an apple or a banana (contains iron and is actually lower in calories than two biscuits).

For lunch, instead of a sandwich, hamburger or hot dog, have a salad. There are countless different kinds of salads, and they are all delicious, filling and nourishing. Most people's idea of salad is a bit of limp lettuce and a soggy tomato or two, but salad making is as much of an art form as cooking, and with nearly as many variations. I truly believe that the less your food is cooked the better it is for you, and in salads you can put practically every raw vegetable and fruit that exists.

If you must eat dessert, then have a yoghurt (great for the intestines), fresh fruit or tinned fruit without the juice.

Teatime is the time of day when most of us need a lift. I do, and that's when a strong urge for something sweet usually comes over me, and with my tea I'll have one or two chocolate digestive biscuits. Needless to say I don't eat them every day – but I do believe in a little sustenance around 4 o'clock. I may have some peanuts or almonds (another fabulous and natural food) or one piece of toast and honey, or some Cheddar cheese and an apple. Then by dinner time I am not so ravenous that I fall upon my food like a fugitive from a concentration camp.

Dinner is for most of us the big meal of the day, perhaps a family gathering or sometimes a social occasion. You may find it hard to deprive yourself while everyone else gets stuck into the chips and the pud, but if you start thinking of eating for energy, vitality and health rather than of dieting, and begin to see the results in your own body, you will soon be able to resist such temptations. A baked potato with a little margarine, besides tasting delicious, is full of iron and calcium and less fattening than chips. (Always eat the skin of a baked potato – it is full of nourishment.)

Obviously you're going to want to have meat sometimes for dinner, but since animal fats are particularly high in cholesterol it is best to cut off all visible fat. Turkey and chicken have fewer calories than beef or lamb, and fish has fewer still. And did you know that you can even eat spaghetti and not gain weight! Pasta, eaten as a main course with a salad, is a well balanced meal with about the same calorie count as meat and two vegetables.

One of the best ways I know of losing weight is to push yourself away from the table having only eaten half a portion of everything. Try it for a week – you will definitely lose pounds.

Vital protein

To keep healthy, your body needs protein of the highest quality. Protein supplies energy and amino acids, which are essential building blocks for the growth, maintenance and repair of the body and cells. Three billion cells in your body need repairing constantly, and only protein can repair them. It cannot be stored and you can't take it in pill form, so you must eat a substantial amount every day. Protein *makes* skin, hair and nails. Don't forget it!

Some of the value of protein may be lost through cooking which can destroy essential amino acids, so it is advisable to undercook rather than overcook all food containing protein (and all food in general).

High protein foods include eggs, meat, fish, liver, milk, cheese, pulses (especially lentils), nuts (especially almonds).

Body power and vitamins

Without vitamins we would die or fall prey to all manner of illnesses. Years ago we got all the natural vitamins we needed in our daily diet. But now our food has become over-processed and over-refined. Preservative and colouring is added to make foods look more attractive to the consumer and last longer on the supermarket shelf, and many of the natural nutrients are removed. Because so much of the food we eat today is deficient in this way, it is advisable to supplement our diets with extra vitamins.

The main vitamins
Vitamin A helps to repair body tissue and prevent skin dryness and ageing. It is also essential for eyesight.

Vitamin A is a fat soluble vitamin, which means it can be stored in the liver and does not need replenishing every day. (The other fat soluble vitamins are D and E.)

Best sources of Vitamin A: apricots, broccoli, butter, chicken, lamb, liver, kidneys, parsley, papaya, spinach, watercress.

Vitamin B complex is a combination of most of the B vitamins. These are not found in most foods but I believe it is essential to take them, especially if you are under any sort of stress (aren't we all?) or if you are pregnant. They are water soluble, therefore they cannot be stored in the body and should be replenished daily.

Best sources: brewers' yeast is the most natural source of Vitamin B and the easiest to take. Others are leaf vegetables, liver and kidneys, and wholegrain bread.

Vitamin C. I swear by Vitamin C. I take it daily and triple the dose in winter, when the body is susceptible to colds and flu. If you smoke it is essential, but to my mind its healing and rejuvenative properties have not yet been sufficiently appreciated by the majority of doctors. I only get a couple of colds a year, if that, and I put it down to building up my resistance by proper eating and plenty of Vitamin C.

Vitamin C was discovered to be essential in the diet when years ago sailors on long trips overseas developed scurvy, a disease involving loss of teeth and bleeding gums. Eventually it was discovered that a lime a day kept the scurvy at bay, and the disease started to decline.

Although some good synthetic Vitamin C is on the market, there is no substitute for the natural vitamin found in rose hips, orange and lemon juice. Dr Irwin Stone, the leading authority on Vitamin C, claims that if we take enough of it we can not only prevent colds but also control the ageing process, heart disease and cancer – good enough reasons for me to take lashings of it!

Vitamin C cannot be stored in the body and must be utilized immediately. According to Dr Stone, between 2000 and 4000 milligrams a day is the right amount, but if I feel I am getting a cold or have been smoking heavily I will take up to 9000. It is highly perishable both in food and pill form, so as many as possible of the foods in the list below should be eaten raw. If cooked they should be put in a double boiler or steamed so as not to destroy the nutritional value. Vitamin C should be taken several times a day, always with food or a drink – such as milk or fruit juice.

Best sources: oranges, lemons, grapefruit, tangerines, pineapple, strawberries, blackcurrants, papaya, cherries, alfalfa sprouts, broccoli, Brussels sprouts, cabbage, cauliflower, parsley, green peppers and watercress.

Vitamin D is the calcium vitamin, necessary for building healthy bones and teeth. Since like Vitamin A it is stored in the liver, it does not have to be taken as often as Vitamin C. (I personally prefer to take calcium tablets – I like the taste – rather than Vitamin D pills.)

Best sources: eggs, salmon, fish such as mackerel, herrings and sardines, cod liver and halibut liver oil (if you can bear it). The sun is a great source of Vitamin D – in moderation, of course.

Vitamin E is my favourite vitamin and one which I take often, although its powers have not yet been proved conclusively. It has been called the youth vitamin, since it helps prevent ageing, and also combats bad circulation and liver problems. Those who lead a particularly stressful life should always take Vitamin E, and it is even claimed by some to increase sexual potency in both men and women. It is an excellent aid in the healing of scars: the oil from one of the capsules should be applied daily to any scar tissue.

The recommended daily dose of Vitamin E is 400 units.
Best sources: wheatgerm and wholemeal bread and flour, sunflower seeds, avocados, olive oil, eggs, apples, carrots and cabbage.

Lecithin

Lecithin is vitally important in assisting the body to burn up fat, which it does faster than any of the other nutrients or vitamins. It keeps the fat in your body moving when you are on a diet or just eating normally. It has many other functions but is particularly good for the liver, brain and nerves.

Lecithin can be taken in either capsule or powdered grain form (the latter sprinkled on cereals or in drinks).
Foods rich in lecithin: soya beans and oil, vegetable and unrefined oils, egg yolk, beef heart, liver, wheatgerm.

Drinking water

Do you like drinking ex-sewage? Does the idea of imbibing cleaned up dishwater, however many times it has been recycled, fill you with distaste? If so you are one of many who are getting around to the idea that the water supply of much of our Western world is no longer what it might be.

The Queen must know something. She never travels anywhere in the world without an adequate supply of her favourite bottled water. And the recent spate of horror stories emanating from the United States, where main water sources in certain towns were found to contain cancer-causing chemicals leaked in from nearby factories, is enough to make me think very seriously of just what other nasty ingredients are contained in so-called 'pure water'.

True, in Britain our water is recycled at least eight times. But the fact remains that there is only a limited amount of potable water available on this earth. Once drunk where does it go? The thought does not thrill me, nor does the knowledge that many chemicals and minerals are added to the water supply to make it safe. That is why I and many others wherever possible drink bottled, chemical-free water. It is expensive, yes, but perhaps in the final analysis the expense will have been worth it.

If you must drink tap water always let the tap run for a good while first thing in the morning. It has stood in the pipes overnight and may have picked up metallic particles from the pipes and fixtures. That doesn't thrill me either.

The magic of lemon

While most fruits are beneficial to good health, first place must got to the lemon. Apart from being one of the richest sources of Vitamin C, it also has the following benefits.

Lemon juice is one of the best aids to digestion, and is recommended for losing weight as it has virtually no calories. It makes good salad dressing.

Lemon cleanses the liver and tones up the heart.

High blood pressure, bad circulation, distended veins, fragile blood vessels, all these troubles can be treated with a lemon cure.

Lemon and hot water first thing in the morning is an excellent cleanser and purifier, and very good to take while dieting.

Lemon juice rinse for the hair makes it shine and glow. Half a lemon rubbed on the elbows whitens and softens them.

Use grated lemon rind in salads. It tastes good and is excellent for you.

Hot water, lemon and honey is an old fashioned but excellent cure for a sore throat.

45

The dreaded dieting

Diets are on-again off-again, bores always. Nothing is more dreary than being on one continuous diet. Food is wonderful, eating is a joy. How ghastly to have to curtail it in favour of our figures!

I eat well. Very well. I rarely stint myself on what I want, and yet I keep my weight more or less constant between 115 and 120lb, and why? Because I changed my eating habits.

It wasn't so difficult really. Several years ago I just stopped eating stodge – buns, puddings, custards, trifles, jelly, heavy fried food, thick floury sauces, nasty teeth-rotting soft drinks, sweets, toffees, cakes, doughnuts hardly ever touch my lips. I *do* however occasionally eat chocolates, fudge, ice cream, particularly tempting desserts and sauté potatoes. I don't believe in total deprivation, but the foods in the first list I mention do nothing nutritionally and merely put on weight, while those in the second group do have some food value and therefore can be eaten in moderation. And let me stress the moderation. Although I don't usually eat dessert or sweets, there will be the odd evening when I passionately crave a lump of fudge or a bar of nut milk chocolate, and I often yield to temptation at a party or dinner where the dessert is just too delicious to refuse. Also I would rather drink wine than eat sweet things, and it's a fact of life that you cannot have your wine and eat your cake too!

Changing your eating habits, although it cannot be achieved overnight, is essential for maintaining not only your health but your looks too. Stop next time you reach for the biscuits, cakes or macaroni in the supermarket; fill your basket with nuts, cheese, fruit, yoghurt, apple juice instead. Start finding out the nutritional values of different foods. Your aim must be to cut sugar and starch (carbo-hydrates) from your diet as much as possible and substitute protein and fats.

Amazingly enough this form of eating really works and is the way that weight loss can be not only achieved, but maintained. Also, the basic craving for sweets and carbohydrates, if left unsatisfied, will eventually turn to a desire for more health-giving food. Remember it isn't the *quantity* but the *quality* of the food you eat that puts on the pounds.

46

Here is a list of foods low in carbohydrates that you can eat often without gaining weight:

Artichokes	Guinea fowl
Asparagus	Ham
Avocado pears	Hamburgers
Bean sprouts	Kidneys
Beans, green	Lamb
Beef	Lettuce
Blackberries	Liver
Bologna	Liverwurst
Brains	Lobster
Broccoli	Margarine
Butter	Mayonnaise
Cabbage	Melon
Cauliflower	Mushrooms
Celeriac	Olives
Celery	Oysters
Cheese	Plums
Cherries	Pork
Chicken	Rabbit, stewed
Clams	Radishes
Cottage cheese	Raspberries
Crab	Rhubarb
Cream	Sardines
Cream cheese	Sauerkraut
Cucumber	Shrimps
Duck	Spinach
Eggplant (aubergine)	Spring greens
Eggs	Steak
Fat (vegetable fat, oil)	Tongue
Fish (all kinds)	Tuna fish
Frankfurters	Turkey
French salad dressing	Veal

Some breakfast menus low in carbohydrates

Small glass grapefruit juice
Tomato and herb omelette (2 eggs) made in non-stick frying
  pan without oil or fat
2 slices bacon
1 slice wholewheat toast and pat of butter
Tea or coffee with milk (no sugar)

2 poached eggs
1 slice wholemeal toast
1 tablespoon butter
1 small sausage
Tea or coffee with milk (no sugar)

1 slice bacon and 1 slice liver
1 slice wholemeal toast
1 tablespoon butter
$\frac{1}{2}$ cup *drained* orange slices (tinned)
Tea or coffee with milk (no sugar)

$\frac{1}{2}$ cup diced melon
$\frac{1}{2}$ cup rice crispies with cream (oh joy! no sugar, though)
2 boiled eggs
Tea or coffee with milk (no sugar)

Small glass tomato juice
2 scrambled eggs
2 slices smoked salmon
1 slice toast with cream cheese
Tea or coffee with milk (no sugar)

$\frac{1}{2}$ grapefruit
2 fried eggs (in a non-stick pan)
1 slice of ham
2 slices rye crisp and butter
Tea or coffee with milk (no sugar)
These breakfasts are extremely filling, so you will find that
you are not ravenous for lunch and dinner.

Some low carbohydrate menus for lunch and dinner
With all of these you may have either a glass of dry white
wine or 1 medium vodka, gin or Scotch – yippee!

$\frac{1}{2}$ avocado pear with oil and vinegar dressing
2 slices turkey
1 small baked potato with butter
1 small apple
Tea or coffee

Small bowl onion soup with 2 teaspoons grated Parmesan
    cheese
2 small lamb chops, grilled
6 asparagus spears with hollandaise sauce
1 pear
Tea or coffee

Roast lamb with rosemary
Endive salad with French dressing
$\frac{1}{2}$ cup cooked spinach
$\frac{1}{2}$ cup orange sections
Tea or coffee

1 hamburger (4oz) grilled
$\frac{1}{2}$ cup broccoli cooked in butter
Tomato and cucumber salad with dressing
Tea or coffee with cream or milk

2 small slices roast beef
1 tablespoon horseradish sauce
4oz French beans in butter
4oz raspberries and cream
Tea or coffee

Grilled sole
Boiled new potatoes (2)
Fruit salad with cream
Tea or coffee

$\frac{1}{2}$ tin sardines
Cucumber and tomato salad
1 salt biscuit and 4oz Cheddar cheese
1 peach
Tea or coffee

Roast chicken
1 small baked potato in jacket with butter
4oz cooked cauliflower
Small slice of melon
Tea or coffee

1oz pâté
1 water biscuit and butter
2 slices ham
Small cucumber salad
Small bunch of grapes
Tea or coffee

Fasting

Do not underestimate the benefits of fasting. Pooh-poohed by many as dangerous or faddish, fasting is nevertheless one of the easiest and surest ways to lose weight quickly. There is of course the possibility that you may put the pounds back on again if you return instantly to your old eating habits, but if you are even slightly disciplined you will not do this.

Fasting has been used as a cleansing and rehabilitating process for centuries. A fast of one or two days five or six times a year can be extremely beneficial to your skin and bodily functions. It gives the stomach, intestines and liver a chance to rest for a while.

Ideally during a classic fast you eat nothing whatsoever. But, and it is a big but, it is *essential* to drink at least 6 glasses of distilled water at intervals throughout the day – not tap water, which is full of chemical and fluoride additives (see page 43). Any of the recognized brands of mineral water or just plain soda water are OK. During this fast, which should not last for more than two days, you will lose 2–6lb a day, depending on the amount of fluid you retain and the extent to which you are overweight.

A modified fast is to eat nothing, but to drink 2 glasses of water and 3 cups of tea with a teaspoonful of honey and a small wedge of lemon each day. This will give you some illusion that you are not depriving yourself totally, and also the honey will give you a certain amount of energy. It is still possible to lose 2–5lb a day on this method.

A third method of fasting involves taking fruit juice only, and this means *fresh* squeezed juice, not the frozen or bottled stuff which has at least twice as many calories. I suggest a mixture of orange and grapefruit juice.

When you finish the fast it is advisable to return to normal eating habits gradually. Your stomach will have benefited from its rest, so treat it gently. The first day, for breakfast, have a cup of tea with honey and a small slice of melon, for lunch a plain yoghurt with a sliced apple and prunes. (You may need the prunes after a fast, by the way.) For dinner have a small piece of grilled chicken or fish and a small salad.

If you continue with this moderate eating pattern for the rest of the week there is no reason why you should not feel your waistband considerably looser by the end of the week, and hear those wonderful words from your friends 'You look great – have you lost weight?'

Crash diets

I don't recommend these particularly but if, like me, you sometimes return from a holiday and find that either the cleaners have shrunk your clothes or you've put on a few nasty pounds, a crash diet is sometimes the quickest way to get it off. Here are some tried and trusted ones. But again, *not* more than two or three days.

Egg diet
Six eggs a day, cooked any way you like (if fried use a non-stick pan and just a trace of vegetable oil). I usually hard-boil at least two of my daily ration so that if I can't wait for mealtimes I can munch on a hard-boiled egg. Try not to have salt with them (if you must, then use sea salt or celery salt). With this diet it is easy to go out to a restaurant since you can always order a small omelette. Don't forget the 6 glasses of water a day.

All-purpose salad diet

Take 2 small apples, diced; 1 green pepper, diced; 2 carrots, shredded; a handful of raisins; 1 orange, sectioned; and 4oz of raw cauliflower cut into small bits. Mix in a large salad bowl with a dressing made of $\frac{1}{2}$ cup plain yoghurt and a tablespoonful of honey. Refrigerate in the bowl and eat throughout the day at well-spaced intervals or when hunger pangs threaten.

Cottage cheese and melon diet

Take half a cantaloupe melon and put a tablespoonful of cottage cheese in the cavity. Have it three times a day for breakfast, lunch and dinner – and 6 glasses of water, of course.

Turkey (or chicken) and grapefruit diet

Poultry is quite low in calories – a medium slice contains approximately 40 calories, and half a grapefruit approximately 20. Sixty calories per meal three times a day adds up to under 200 calories a day, which is a definite crash diet in anybody's language. Don't try it for longer than three days.

Green grape diet

This is a simple but effective diet. Eat nothing else but green grapes, as many as you want as often as you want. Do not eat the skin or the pips. You can chew them up but should then spit them out, otherwise you could become a touch constipated.

Banana and milk diet

An oldie but a goodie (I lost 7lb on this when I first went under contract to 20th Century Fox as a chubby teenager).

Breakfast   1 banana, 1 glass of milk
Lunch   1 banana, 1 glass of milk
Tea $\frac{1}{2}$ glass milk
Dinner   2 bananas, 1 glass of milk

Eat nothing else – drink only water.

Cheese and tomato diet

I love cheese and I like tomatoes a lot too. The best kind of cheese for this diet is either Mozzarella or another Italian cheese called dolcelatte, but you could also use Edam (60 calories an ounce), Roquefort (70 calories an ounce), or Cheddar (115 calories per ounce). A small tomato contains about 20 calories. Simply eat 3oz of cheese and 6 tomatoes at regular intervals throughout the day. You can put a little vinegar and celery salt on the tomato to spruce it up a bit. Don't forget the water!

Don't make the mistake of thinking that you can mix these crash diets, for example have a banana and milk diet one day and then the second day change to an egg diet. This won't work. The whole effect of a crash diet is that your body burns off the excess fat because of the sameness of it; it does not work if you chop and change.

Crash diets

Here are five ways to tell if you are overweight:

1. *The pinch test* Bend your arm and see if you can pinch more than an inch of flesh under your arm between your elbow and shoulder. If you can you are overweight.

2. *The tape-measure test* Subtract your waist measurement (in inches) from your height (in inches). You may be overweight if your total is less than 36. For example, if you are 5ft (i.e. 60in) tall and your waist measures 28in, 60–28 = 32 = obese.

3. *The ruler test* Lying flat on your back, place a ruler lengthwise on your stomach. The ruler should touch both your ribs and pubic bone.

4. *The ideal weight test* If your weight exceeds that given for your height in the table below, you are overweight.

5. *The absolute acid test* Look at yourself, naked, in a full-length mirror. Do you like what you see?

Your desirable weight in pounds

(women 25 years of age and over,* without clothing)

Height	Small frame	Medium frame	Large frame
4'8"	89–95	93–104	101–116
4'9"	91–98	95–107	103–119
4'10"	93–101	98–110	106–122
4'11"	96–104	101–113	109–125
5'0"	99–107	104–116	112–128
5'1"	102–110	107–119	115–131
5'2"	105–113	110–123	118–135
5'3"	108–116	113–127	122–139
5'4"	111–120	117–132	126–143
5'5"	115–124	121–136	130–147
5'6"	119–128	125–140	134–151
5'7"	123–132	129–144	138–155
5'8"	127–137	133–148	142–160
5'9"	131–141	137–152	146–165
5'10"	135–145	141–156	150–170

*If you are between the ages of 18 and 25, subtract one pound for each year less than 25.
Adapted from Metropolitan Life Insurance statistics.

Skin Care

If the eyes are the mirror of the soul, the skin is the barometer of one's mental and physical health.

The most beautiful thing about a new baby is its skin: fresh, moist, firm, perfect. We take the utmost care with a baby's skin. We pamper it with oils, lotions and powders, with special soaps and creams. We lavish care and attention on every crack and crevice of the beautiful babe – and what happens? She gets to be three or four and we think she doesn't need pampering any longer. For the next fifteen or twenty years of her life, skin care consists of keeping the grime off. A good scrub with hard soap and water morning and night and lots of hot baths, and that's it. How sad that through neglect and ignorance and just normal everyday living this previously beautiful baby skin will eventually lose its lustre, its texture and its beauty.

Suddenly at the age of twenty or twenty-five our growing baby girl realizes that her skin is not what it was, so she starts doing something about it. If she is diligent and clever enough perhaps she will be able to erase slightly the ravages of time and environment, but there is no magic cream or formula that can ever fully restore the bloom to a faded complexion. Don't despair, however. It is *never* too late to start caring for your skin.

Skin is made up of two layers, the epidermis and the dermis. The epidermis is the outer layer, the one the world sees and you fret over, because it shows all the excesses of lack of rest, too much food, and mental and physical stress. Under the epidermis is the dermis. It cannot be seen, but it is here that pimples, acne or any of the other plagues begin days before you are aware of them.

The dermis is living tissue composed of billions of cells in a lake of liquid with roughly the same salt content as the sea. Each cell is separated from the other by a membrane

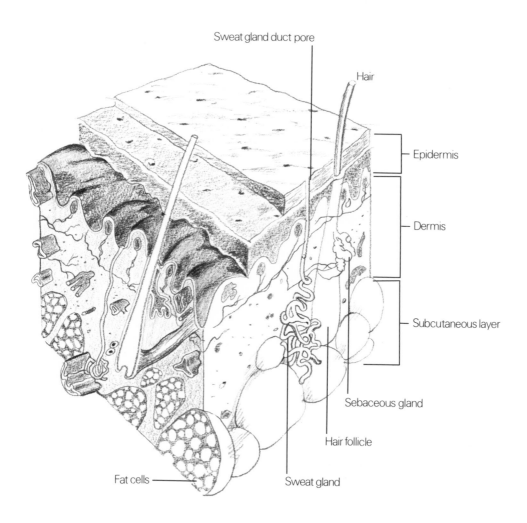

Sweat gland duct pore

Hair

Epidermis

Dermis

Subcutaneous layer

Sebaceous gland

Hair follicle

Fat cells

Sweat gland

through which nutrients and respiratory gases continually pass, enabling the cells to grow and reproduce. The various functions of the skin are to protect the body from invasion by bacteria or virus; to regulate temperature; to eliminate (along with the kidneys) the waste products; and to convey information about the outside world via thousands of complicated sensory nerve endings.

The skin registers pleasure and pain, and can reveal the emotional and physical state of the whole body. It is closely interrelated with all the other organisms of the body. To function well the skin must carry out its duties unimpaired by poor nutrition, bad circulation, illness, pollution or lack of oxygen, all of which hinder its efficiency.

The millions of cells in the skin contain water which cushions the skin and keeps it soft. When the cells shrink through too much sun or through age, they become unable to hold enough water and it escapes, giving the skin a dried-out appearance. That's when the skin can look like a prune instead of a plum (they're both the same fruit, but one contains moisture and the other doesn't). One of the main problems is keeping enough water in the skin. Dried-up skin comes from underactive sebaceous glands which, as a result of hormone imbalance or vitamin deficiencies, do not produce enough oily fluid to lubricate and prevent excess water loss.

Looking after your skin

The soap and water controversy

Recently I have had a re-think about soap and water. For years I didn't allow a drop of either to touch my face, but some time ago I started to experiment, using an extremely mild non-alkaline soap two or three times a week. I was fanatical in rinsing off the soap with warm water at least thirty times, as the residue of soap is what causes scaling, drying skin and that taut, stretched feeling. I found that far from cracking-up my skin started to look better, and it certainly felt cleaner.

Soap and water care is of course a bone of contention with skin experts, but more dermatologists now agree that using a well formulated non-alkaline soap is one of the best ways of keeping the skin thoroughly clean. But it *must* be an extremely mild and gentle soap made specially for the face, and it *must* always be thoroughly rinsed off.

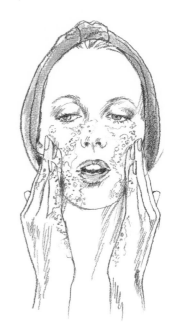

Basic regime for care of the face

Remove make-up with tissue or cotton-wool pads and a liquid remover. Soap and water cannot remove make-up thoroughly – contrary to what you may have heard – in fact it may even set the make-up on your skin and seal it in.

If you wear make-up you must always use a cleansing cream or emulsion to remove it every night. Make-up can block pores, cause irritation and contribute towards the formation of pimples. Rub the remover gently in a circular motion upwards from the neck until the last cotton-wool pad shows no trace of make-up.

Wash face and neck with soap. Work up a lather, rub gently for about 30 seconds. Rinse thoroughly with warm water – as many as thirty times.

Dry face with a clean towel. Never use a towel on your face that someone else has used; keep a special towel for your face, even if you have to wash it every day. If a clean towel is not available, blot face with tissues.

While your skin is still damp, moisten a cotton-wool pad with toner or astringent (depending on skin type) and dab over the face and neck. The point of using a tonic after cleansing is to remove every trace of cleanser, oil, dead cells and dirt.

For dry skin use a very gentle alcohol-free toner: there are several good ones on the market, or you can use glycerine and rosewater, which is cheap and available from any chemist. For oily skin an alcohol-based tonic is needed to make certain that all grease is removed.

While the skin is still damp from toner, apply moisturizer liberally all over face, and don't forget the neck. There are many good moisturizers on the market. Most of them contain oil in water emulsions, and seal in the precious moisture your skin needs to remain youthful and soft. Since the moisturizer holds the water in the skin, it keeps the outer layers plumped up. Water is what softens the skin, not oil. Since our bodies are 60 per cent water, it is no wonder that water in so many ways is a little miracle. As we get older, production of sebum, the skin's natural moisturizer, slows down and our skin starts to dry up more; this is when central heating and gas and electric fires dry up the skin dangerously.

Allow moisturizer 30 seconds to penetrate the skin thoroughly, and then apply make-up.

I am a strong believer in the benefit of make-up as a protection against the grime and pollution in our environment. Contrary to what many people think, far from harming your skin, make-up can and does protect it from the elements. I seldom venture out into the city streets without a thin base on my skin, even if I don't get around to making up my eyes and lips.

Retaining the peaches-and-cream skin of childhood and early youth takes a certain amount of hard work and discipline. It is no more time-consuming than cleaning your teeth, but just as necessary. You can always get false teeth, but a new skin? Never!

Common skin problems

Skin problems – blackheads, whiteheads, pimples, spots – all begin in either the oil ducts or hair follicles. Each hair follicle is served by a sebaceous gland which pumps oil (or sebum) straight on to the surface of the skin. Problems usually start in the early teenage years when the oil glands get bigger and also start working harder, events triggered by the body's manufacture of hormones. If too much sebum is secreted the hair follicle gets blocked, the normal healthy bacteria which we have on our skin all the time turn nasty, and the acne-producing bacteria which in normal conditions are dormant, break down the sebum to fatty acids which cause inflammation. Trouble begins to show outwardly in the form of a spot if the infection breaks through the follicle wall and destroys surrounding tissue.

Many women and girls have some kind of low-grade acne condition, with blackheads and some occasional spots. Acne can start at any age between puberty and menopause – we don't know why. Women in their twenties and thirties respond to the same treatment as teenagers. If you have a tendency to acne, don't use a moisturizer, or if you must, use only a very light liquid type. Anything you put on your skin can plug up the pores and cause blackheads, so if you break out in spots don't put grease or creams on your face and use make-up with as little oil in it as possible. You can't prevent break-outs but you *can* minimize the problems.

Make-up protects the skin but it must be removed very carefully to ensure that the pores do not become blocked, thus causing skin problems.

Cures for skin problems

There are some excellent products available for spots, acne, whiteheads, pimples and all the other skin aggravations which, however much care one takes with one's skin, are still liable to occur now and again. (Usually when you least want them.) Here are some of them.

Clearasil Cream Medication   A flesh-tinted spot cream containing an anti-bacterial agent which dries spots, and sulphur which dries and peels the skin.

Swiss Bio-Facial Treatment Cream   A colourless cream containing chlorhexidine which kills bacteria.

Face Savers Cream Medication   Contains sulphur and resorcinol, which is drying and helps to peel spots.

pHiso-Ac   A flesh-tinted cream which contains sulphur and resorcinol.

Trisonovin   A flesh-tinted cream also containing sulphur and resorcinol.

Below: a blemish-free skin, thanks to the careful and correct application and removal of make-up and judicious use of skin medication when necessary.

*A perfect example of a
beautiful hand and well
cared for manicured nails.*

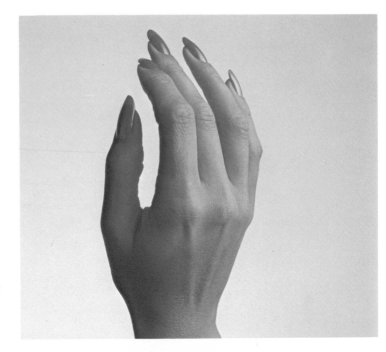

*Talking on the phone while
having a bath on the set of
a Twenties movie. Few of
us can be lucky enough to
have an original 1920s
bath tub like this, but we
should all ensure that bath-
time is a relaxing and
beautifying time for the
body.*

Both my daughters Tara and Katyana have benefited from the skin care regime I started them on when they were babies. Above, Tara and I are both wearing Victorian camisoles bought from an antique market.

I like often to change my look and here are four variations.
Casual daytime

Cocktail or disco

The big evening look: the long . . .

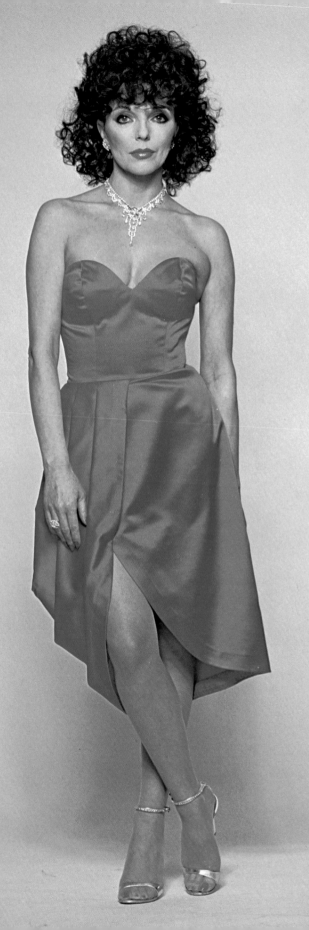

. . . and the short of it

New skin for old

As new skin cells form and travel to the outer surface of the skin, they lose their natural moisture and eventually become dry, scaly flakes. These dead cells need to be sloughed off, and certain areas of the body should be scrubbed regularly in order to hasten this process and to revitalize the new skin. For this you will need:

A loofah This is perfect for sloughing off the dead cells on legs, arms and back. It should be used once or twice a week, with a circular motion, while you are in the bath or shower.

A pumice stone Elbows, knees and soles of feet need somewhat harsher treatment and for this a pumice stone can be used judiciously. Wet a bit of this abrasive stone, rub with non-alkaline soap and go over rough spots, again with a circular motion.

For the face, a much more modified version of the two methods above should be used in the form of face masks, face packs, and mud packs, pore cleansing scrubs and buff puffs. There are so many different types of face masks and scrubs around that a small book could be written about them alone. In my view a simple face pack or mask which deep-cleanses the pores and gets rid of dead cells should be used once every seven to ten days at least. Some of the most widely used are given below.

Facial scrubs These are slightly abrasive, sandy textured creams which when rubbed with a circular motion into the skin slough off dead cells. They are not recommended for very fine skins.

Pore grains There are many brands on the market. They work abrasively but gently on the skin, removing dead cells, loosening blackheads and pimples, and smoothing out tiny lines. One can also use sugar for this purpose – it's cheaper but harder on the skin. I would like to emphasize that I don't recommend pore grains for fine or delicate skin. I myself do not use them, but I do think they are often necessary for oily or medium skin.

The Buf-Puf A recent innovation from the States, the Buf-Puf is a loose weave, rather scratchy plastic white sponge which is excellent for removing dead cells and polishing the skin's surface. It should be used two or three times a week: work up a lather with a mild soap, rub for *no more* than 8–10 seconds on each area (never around the eyes) and rinse very thoroughly.

Peel-off masks   These masks are applied or brushed all over the face. They are usually made of a colourless gel-like lotion which as it dries has a tightening effect on the skin. When dry the mask is peeled off, and the skin underneath should be soft, moist and definitely smoother. There are no long-term effects but the benefit will be noticeable over a period of twenty-four hours. Use about once every seven to ten days, alternating with a face pack.

Beauty salon treatments and facials   I do not really see the need for these. I have had about four facials in my life, and to tell the truth have found little or no difference in my skin from the care I give it myself. But for those who would like to try a do-it-yourself version, here is a quick and easy method.

The home facial

(Do not forget to include your neck and throat in all the following precedures.)

Clean your face with make-up remover or lotion, massaging it on your skin for five minutes then removing it gently with cotton wool.

Steam your face. Take a pot of boiling water and place it on a hotplate on a low table. Sitting in front of the steaming pot, take a large towel and make a tent over your head. Holding the edge of the towel about six inches in front of your forehead, lean over the pot, but keep at least one foot away – if you get too close you can burn your skin or come out looking a bit lobsterish. After ten minutes pat your face dry.

Apply a mask. (You can use either a proprietary brand or a natural home-made one, see pages 78 and 79.) After ten minutes, remove the mask with damp cotton-wool balls. Try not to talk or move your face while the mask is on (take the phone off the hook!).

Spray your face all over with a fine mist of Evian water or dab with damp cotton wool. Gently pat your skin dry and then apply a light moisturizer.

If possible, do not apply make-up for several hours after your facial. Let your skin breathe.

Watch all those bad habits

Don't frown or squint or raise your eyebrows. Although wrinkles, like Christmas, will eventually arrive, you can prevent the ones on the forehead by frowning as little as possible. You can always see the difference on the foreheads of those who frown and those who don't.

Don't stretch your face by pulling or tugging at it; leave it alone, except for skin care and make-up. Be particularly careful about applying make-up under the eyes, the most sensitive area: dot your make-up on gently. And try to sleep without a pillow. The indentations in your face the next morning from that comfy feather pillow could become permanent.

Skin reflects your mental and physical health more than any other part of your body, so you should give it particular care. And make-up, however skilfully applied, cannot hide the signs of stress on your face or the fact that you've been over-indulging in booze, cream buns or late nights. Do so if you must – but in moderation.

Some tips for winter skin care

We often forget that cold weather can be just as harmful to the skin as the burning rays of the sun.

Protect lips and under eyes with a chap stick and under-eye cream. The tissue around the eyes is extremely vulnerable, and usually the place where lines first appear. I have even seen ten year olds with lines under their eyes, and I'm sure it wasn't from too much TV!

Always protect against the drying effects of wind with a strong barrier cream or moisturizer, and apply these under make-up too.

You should always wear sunglasses in very bright wintry sunlight and especially in snow. Squint lines occur just as much from the reflection of snow as they do from sand and water.

Cellulite

Cellulite is a thick puckered fat that develops around hips, upper arms, thighs and stomachs. The fat is mixed with body wastes and is harder and more compressed than fat on other parts of the body. It accumulates gradually and then presses through the skin's outer tissue making the skin look something like a quilted orange peel.

Cellulite fat has a variety of causes – hormonal problems, constipation, bad diet, lack of exercise. Constricting clothing, tight tights or boots can also contribute to the formation of cellulite by preventing proper circulation.

The accumulation of cellulite is a problem that besets many women; it often starts with the onset of puberty and develops slowly and insidiously, but usually does not begin to show until after the age of thirty-five. Once it appears it is extremely difficult to get rid of, but it can be reduced and often prevented with a combination of diet, exercise and at-home care.

Diet

A diet to avoid or reduce cellulite build-up must be based on lean proteins: grilled meats, fish, eggs, chicken and cottage cheese.

You should take no additional salt and avoid salty foods: salt causes the body to retain water.

You must cut down on carbohydrates and cut out sugar and sweets entirely.

Never skip a meal. Your body will be much healthier if it is regularly digesting moderate sized meals rather than one or two large ones.

You should try to eliminate or drastically reduce alcoholic beverages, which are high in sugar content and also put strain on the body's elimination programme. Drink mineral water or soda water with a slice of lemon.

Drink at least one to two quarts of water a day – more if you can. Water aids digestion and keeps your system clean (but see page 43 for my personal reservations about tap water).

Circulation

Don't wear tights that constrict your waist and hips.
Don't wear tight girdles, belts or garters.
Avoid knee-length stockings with elasticized tops.
Don't wear tight boots.
Don't sit with your legs crossed.

Exercise

The benefits of mild, regular exercise are twofold: it stimulates circulation which helps decongest the cellulitic area, and firms up the sagging muscles caused by a sedentary lifestyle or simply by the normal ageing process.

The magic egg
The egg is one of the oldest known natural beauty products in existence. It is said that Cleopatra used white of egg on her face as a mask (while bathing in asses' milk, no doubt).

Here are a couple of recipes for beauty treatments using this simple little object.

Nourishing face mask (this can be used every other day)
1 egg yolk
1 teaspoon almond oil
Mix together; apply and leave on the face for 10–30 minutes. Cream may also be added to make it even more nutritious, and you can use the whole egg instead of the yolk alone. (The egg yolk contains lecithin, one of the most important nutrients, and also protein, which is why it is exceptionally beneficial to the skin.) Experiment to find out what most benefits your skin.

Egg and yeast mask
1 egg yolk
1 tablespoon brewers' yeast
1 tablespoon sunflower oil
Mix these together into a smooth paste and apply to the face. Leave for about 15 minutes and rinse off with milk. The yeast stimulates the skin, and with the addition of the egg yolk and oil is a most effective mask.

The magic avocado

Avocados feed the skin from without as well as within. I truly believe they are one of the best beauty foods, and I eat a lot of them. They contain some of the finest natural oil there is.

The recipes below require a ripe avocado, and are easy to prepare in your own kitchen. (You can hasten the ripening process by placing your avocados in a paper bag or wrapping them in aluminium foil.)

Facial cleanser

1 egg yolk
$\frac{1}{2}$ cup milk
$\frac{1}{2}$ peeled ripe avocado, mashed

Beat egg yolk until light and frothy. Add milk and mashed avocado, blend. Apply on squares of cotton. Store in refrigerator between uses.

Skin mask

$\frac{1}{2}$ avocado, peeled, mashed
1 tablespoon honey
$\frac{1}{4}$ cup milk

Blend avocado, honey and milk. Apply to face and neck. Relax for 20 minutes. Remove with tepid water.

Skin smoother

Shell the avocado and scrape the inside peel clean of any fruit. You will feel a slightly abrasive sandy substance which is oily to the touch. Rub it vigorously on your feet, your hands, or wherever you have rough skin. Dead cells seem to slough off instantly, and the oil of the avocado will lubricate and beautify the skin.

Tanning

There is no question about it, nothing makes you look better and healthier than a gorgeous golden tan. To possess one in July or August is to evoke admiration; to be burnished bronze in November or January is to inspire envy.

   A tan is a status symbol today, and has been for the past few decades. Coco Chanel revolutionized fashion in the

On the rare occasions when I do allow my face to be in the sun I always keep my hair covered to protect it from lightening and drying out.

Twenties when she appeared with a golden tan, shocking café society to the core. For hundreds of years one of the criteria of female beauty had been a flawless white peaches-and-cream complexion, the paler the better. Then suddenly bronzed, golden skin became the goal of all, rich and poor alike. To be tanned denoted wealth: it implied a life of luxury, yachts, private beaches, sybaritic living. It made you look thinner, sexier and healthier, maximizing your defects and giving an illusion of wellbeing.

But the damage which that wonderful sun does to your tender epidermis – the only one you have – is nothing short of catastrophic over a long period. I have observed closely over the years the difference in the skin of those of my friends and acquaintances who bake in the sun often, and those who do so either judiciously or hardly at all. I have to admit that after the age of about thirty the difference is staggering.

By all means sunbathe in moderation (Vitamin D is generated by the sun and is very necessary) but *always* with the proper protection for your face, body and hair. Try to avoid the hours between 11am and 2pm when the damaging ultra-violet rays are at their strongest, and keep your face shaded by a visor or straw hat always. The face is the most delicate part of the body in terms of skin, and the first to show the ravages of the sun. One can always by the application of a little judicious tan make-up and blusher give the illusion of a tan to the face, but it is practically impossible to do that to the rest of your body.

What is a sun tan?
A tan is actually your own skin's *protection* against the ultra-violet rays of the sun. These are immensely damaging to the skin, which to protect itself from becoming burned produces a pigment called melanin. It is this substance that turns the skin brown. Over thousands of years those who live in tropical climates or near the equator have developed heavily pigmented dark skin, while those living closer to the north have light complexions. The lighter your skin the less protective pigmentation it contains.

Since skin types differ radically, there is a vast difference in the shade of brown achieved – it may range from nothing more than a pinkish freckled effect in the case of very fair-complexioned people and redheads to the darkest Mediterranean tan in those with olive skins.

The best protection for your skin type

Fair skin is very sensitive; it needs protection constantly, and much care and supervision. Those with very fair skins can never take the sun for granted, and when in the sun should always wear sunglasses and use protective cover for the face. This type of skin should never be given more than $1–1\frac{1}{2}$ hours' exposure to the sun per day.

Sun tan creams give the greatest protection. Apply at least 20 minutes before exposure, and re-apply every hour *even when you are your desired colour!*

    Bergasol High Protection Cream and Gel (a relatively new sun product whose sales have escalated rapidly)

    Hawaiian Tropic Sun Screen

    Estée Lauder Sun Block Creme for the face (even if you wear a hat)

    Ambre Solaire Creme

Normal or medium skin tans evenly and rarely burns. Tanning gels are preferable for this type of skin.

    Bergasol Sun Tanning Lotion

    Coppertone Lotion

    Bain de Soleil by Antoine (my particular favourite)

    Estée Lauder Tanning Cream

Medium skins can take more exposure to the sun but you must still pay strict attention to the re-application of the preparations. And never lie flat out in it for longer than 45 minutes at a time, or you will look like the proverbial lobster.

Dark skin – the lucky ones! This group can abuse their skins in terms of sun more than most, but unless protection is also used cracks and crevices and wrinkles will eventually come. You've all seen those ancient crones in black frocks and headscarves in Mediterranean countries – shrivelled like old prunes, they were once the proud possessors of gorgeous moist Latin skin.

    Oil-based preparations are best for dark skin.

    Hawaiian Tropic Professional Tanning Oil

    Coppertone Tropical Blend Dark Tanning Oil

    Coconut Oil

    Ambre Solaire Oil

Since these products are made of oil they work fast. They contain virtually no sun screens, so should not be used by lighter skins. But I still feel that sun screens are necessary even for those lucky dark-skinned types, because they protect from the dangerous ultra-violet rays.

Last but not least is a preparation I concocted myself when I was younger and naive about the dangers of the sun. It gives a gorgeous glowing tan but I do not recommend that you use it too often, or for fair sensitive skin.

Mix 8 parts of baby oil with 1 part iodine. Shake thoroughly before each application. Apply every hour.

After tan

It is essential to apply *lots* of moisturizer after sunbathing, to counteract the inevitable drying effects of the sun and keep your skin supple and smooth. Needless to say, the areas that need the greatest pampering are the hands, knees, elbows, neck and under the eyes; because there is very little fat under the skin in these places they are the first to lose their elasticity.

Certain areas of skin (shown here unshaded) are more vulnerable to the sun's rays than others.

One last note. Even if you have done *all* the right things in terms of protection – screens, hats and so on – if you don't watch how long you are in the sun it could all be wasted effort. However dark your complexion is, don't stay directly unprotected in the sun for any longer than 4 or 5 hours a day for dark skins, and 2–3 hours for fair.

The damage done to the skin by the sun cannot be overemphasized. Look at the skin on parts of your body where the sun rarely shines (back of arms, buttocks) and you can see that the texture is finer and less wrinkled there. Sun damage builds up over the years, and however much you protect your skin the cumulative effect can never be eradicated.

I personally never allow my face to be in the sun for more than a few minutes at a time. This means that when I am tanned my face is considerably lighter than my body, but since there are so many excellent tan coloured make-up bases available I just mix up the colour I want to match my body shade, and no one knows the difference.

Eye care

By the time you are twenty-five, little lines and wrinkles begin to appear around your eyes. Sometimes they are caused by too much sun, sometimes by dryness.

The tissue around the eyes is different from the skin on the rest of your face; it is thinner and drier and therefore more prone to wrinkling and sagging, so an eye-care product has to be more emollient. The skin around the eyes also benefits from a high concentration of the soluble protein collagen. There are excellent eye-care products on the market, but while you are looking for the one that suits you best you can use Vaseline. It's good for the lashes too, and cheap.

Never manipulate the skin around the eyes, as it stretches very easily. If you apply make-up or cover stick under the eyes be extremely careful not to stretch the skin, and when you powder do so with a fine mist only.

For circles and puffiness under the eyes Soak cotton-wool pads in cold witch hazel, lie down and place on your eyes. Leave for 15 minutes.

For exhausted eyes Lie down for 15 minutes with one of the following on your eyes: witch hazel (as above), cold tea bags (drink the tea first!), slices of fresh cucumber.

For lined eyes Soak cotton-wool pads in warm almond oil and leave on as long as you can – all night if possible (keep in place with an eye mask). A good temporary remover for fine lines is egg white, brushed gently underneath the eyes in a thin film: apply make-up over this when dry. When removing, use lots of cream as egg whites are quite drying. This is good for a special occasion or party effect, but should not be overdone.

Cosmetic surgery

When I first went to Hollywood in the mid-Fifties I came into contact with a group of women who had had their faces 'done'. The effect of this, on an impressionable young girl like myself, was horrifying: I watched with fascination their stretched, mask-like faces, the skin pulled sometimes so tautly around their jaw lines that every time they blinked their mouths curved upward in a rictus smile. I was relieved to return to the more sophisticated shores of Europe, where women over a certain age were not striving all the time to look twenty-three but allowed their inner beauty, wisdom and humour to compensate for the inevitable lessening of their exterior youthfulness.

Because of this, I have always been vehemently against plastic surgery and face lifts.

Today tremendous advances have been made in the area of cosmetic surgery. Many people from all walks of life are investing in new noses, chins and uplifts to give them that coveted youthful look. I do feel, however, that unless it is a question of absolute necessity, to run the risks of even the most minor surgery is foolish. It is also extremely expensive. But for some people, the victims of deformity or accident, cosmetic surgery fully warrants the risk and expense.

But basically I think that it is unnatural and un-necessary. My face and body are all my own work: that of correct diet, exercise, maintenance and – luckily – good genes. I'm sorry to disappoint my critics and detractors but the plastic surgeon's knife has never touched me, and I hope it never will!

Make-up

Cosmetics are the greatest boon to womankind and have been in use for many thousands of years. From the ancient Egyptians with their whipped ostrich eggs and crocodile oil, through the thick lead paint and crushed roots of the sixteenth and seventeenth centuries to the present day, cosmetic technology has improved one thousandfold.

The ancient Egyptians were the first to use make-up almost as an accessory. Especially around the eyes: their style was advanced and even by today's standards highly sophisticated. The 'Cleopatra eye' is in fact becoming fashionable again today. The eye was boldly rimmed with black kohl, painted into an elongated almond shape, and shimmering, iridescent greenish-blue eyeshadow was used to accentuate it, not unlike modern powdered eyeshadows. Theirs however was a little harder to obtain, since it was made from finely ground malachite (a semi-precious stone).

The Egyptians also used nail polish, lipstick, rouge and all manner of creams, lotions and salves, many of which had a double purpose since they were also used as a protection from the elements.

There was a gradual tapering off in the use of cosmetics throughout the centuries, and by Victorian times it was only 'loose' women, or actors and actresses (who were considered no better than they should be) who wore make-up. Victorian ladies had to resort to such devices as pinching their cheeks to make them pink and glowing, and using only the merest smudge of powder to remove the shine from their faces. And woe betide the girl or woman whose artifice was discovered!

The first decade of this century saw the start of make-up being used more openly. By the Roaring Twenties the use of make-up was becoming universal, and cosmetic houses sprang up like mushrooms. Recently it has become very big business indeed. Millions of pounds a year are spent by the cosmetic companies in advertizing and launching new products. In the laboratories, technicians and cosmeticians are constantly working to discover new and better products, and to improve and refine existing ones. Whereas thirty years ago there was a limited number of items a woman could buy for her face, today there are literally thousands of different products.

When your grandmother was a girl, probably all that was available in the way of lotions to use on her face was cold cream or vanishing cream. Moisturizer for example has only been around for about twenty years – whatever did women use before then?

The make-up revolution started shortly after the effects of the austerity following the Second World War were wearing off. From the beginning of the war in 1939 until about 1950, practically nothing new – cosmetically speaking – was brought out. The young woman of 1950 probably used almost exactly the same lipstick, powder, block mascara and foundation cream as her counterpart in 1939.

With the advent of the Fifties the big cosmetic companies like Revlon, Helena Rubenstein, Elizabeth Arden and Max Factor launched on to an eager female population entirely new concepts of face design. Lipstick colours had always been limited to three or four brash shades of bright orange, pillarbox red and dark crimson. Revlon began introducing dozens of new colour shades, and even textures, and the other cosmetic companies followed suit. Frosted lips and matching frosted nail polish with exotic names like 'Fire and Ice', liquid eye liner for the fashionable doe-eyed look, leg make-up, body make-up, liquid eyeshadow in bright colours and lip brushes were all major cosmetic innovations of the early Fifties.

And then in the Sixties another gigantic cosmetic revolution took place. With the advent of the 'Youth

Two different decades, two
different faces. Above:
myself as a teenager
wearing the over-
exaggerated eyebrows, sharp
black eye liner and heavy
lipstick of the Fifties.
Below, in 1968, my lips are
pale and chalky and my
eyes outlined by both upper
and lower false eyelashes.

Culture', the mini skirt, Mary Quant's little girl look, and Vidal Sassoon's avant-garde geometric haircut, a whole new kind of make-up was needed. Along came light, almost translucent bases and foundations, and mascara in a wand or stick, instead of the old cake type which you had to spit on to get it gooey enough to put on your eyelashes. Pale, almost white lipsticks were the rage, false eyelashes above and below the lids which looked as real as your own (if somewhat thicker), frosted gold and silver eyeshadows, bronze face glossers, and those two indispensable items – lip gloss and blusher. What did we do before *they* were invented?

Since the early Sixties the cosmetic companies have brought out more and more new paints and powders and potions each year, and it now seems impossible to believe that there is indeed anything new that could be created in the world of cosmetics.

I have always liked experimenting with cosmetics and in fact always do my own make-up for films, photo sessions and television. I know my face infinitely better than anyone else does, and I know what suits me, what doesn't suit me and how to put it on with expertise and a minimum of fuss. This should be the aim of every woman: to have your make-up routine down to a fine art, and a practical one; to streamline your make-up drawer and make-up tools; and to have experimented sufficiently (in your spare time) to know the good points and the faults of your face well enough to accentuate or detract from them as necessary.

Just remember one thing always – make-up can only look as good as the skin that it goes on, so don't expect miracles if your skin is in bad condition.

Changing shapes

There are four basic face shapes: long, round, oval and square. These shapes can be emphasized or softened by the skilful use of blusher.

The instructions opposite for using blusher to maximum advantage are based on face shape. To do any of them, you need to locate the cushion formed by your cheek when you smile. Place blush in relation to this cushion – above or below, whatever is indicated for your face shape. Be sure to blend the blusher very carefully.

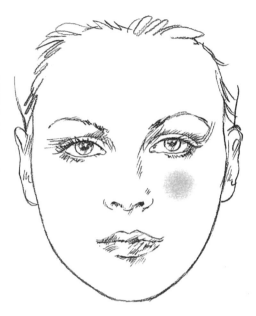

Round face *Apply blusher right on cheek cushion; blend with fingertips. Don't let blush go towards the hairline – keep colour focus near centre of face.*

Oval face *Apply blusher to cheek cushion; extend it up and into temples. Blend carefully.*

Square face *Start colour on top of cheek cushion, then follow along highest part of cheek bone taking blusher not quite to temple line.*

Long face *Apply blusher behind the cheek cushion and up to the temples in the shape indicated. Blend gradually.*

Eyebrows

Eyebrows probably give more character to a face than any other feature. By changing your brow shape you can give your face a totally new look.

Happily the natural thicker eyebrow is more acceptable today than the harsh plucked arch of recent years.

Here are some tips for beautiful brows:

Never try to completely reshape brows. Always follow their natural line, and pluck only if necessary to give a better shape.

Pluck from underneath, but don't be afraid occasionally to pluck a few strays from the top if they are growing wild.

Always use a slant-edged eyebrow tweezer – it's easier to work with.

If you pluck brows after a shower or bath you will find that it does not hurt so much and the hairs come out easily.

If you draw blood, apply a tiny bit of antiseptic lotion with a cotton-wool bud.

If your eyebrows have suffered from a surfeit of over-zealous plucking and consequently won't grow back, you can fill in tiny bald patches where necessary with delicate fine lines, drawn with a very sharp pencil.

Don't 'draw' an eyebrow in one arched stroke. Use light, feathery strokes that look like hairs.

If you have very full brows brush a little Vaseline on them to keep them glossy.

If brows are very heavy and black you may lighten them by bleaching. It is wise to have this done professionally unless you have a very steady hand.

Never colour brows more than two or three shades darker than your natural hair. This is particularly true for blondes who do *not* look good with heavy dark eyebrows.

Putting on false eyelashes
Pick up the eyelashes with tweezers by the far right-hand edge. Apply a thin film of eyelash adhesive to base.

Carefully place the eyelashes on to the eyelid with tweezers, ensuring that the base is as close to the root of your own eyelashes as possible.

With the mascara wand brush your own eyelashes and the false ones together. Who can tell the difference?

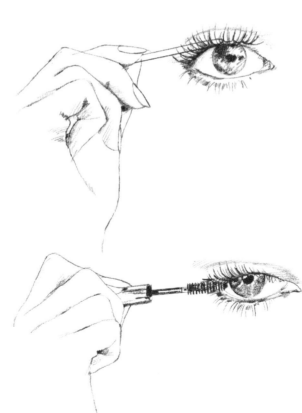

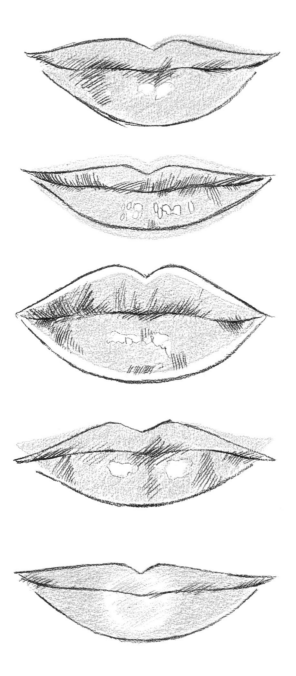

Uneven lips *Balance uneven lips or soften too sharp a bow at centre by outlining the desired shape with a lip pencil. Fill in with colour in a shade close to pencil colour.*

Thin lips *First apply foundation over entire lip area, then outline lips with pencil slightly beyond natural line. Fill in with lip colour inside line.*

Full lips *Apply foundation over lips. Pencil lips just inside lip line and apply lip colour within this line only.*

Droopy lips *Lift them by first covering lip corners with a concealer stick. Blend then powder. Using a lip pencil, extend lip corner up. Fill in with colour.*

Flat lips *To give a plumper look apply colour over entire lips except on very centre. Fill in centre space with a lighter, shimmery colour. Aim for a subtle look; don't make the line between the two colours obvious.*

Lips

Lips can be changed more than any other feature, and can be transformed by the clever use of lipstick. Lipstick or gloss is the most flattering of all make-up – it brings out the colour of the eyes, accentuates the skin tone, and is simply attractive in its own right if you use a pretty colour.

Basic make-up tools

It is easy to get confused when you go into a department store and see thousands of different kinds of beauty aids, creams, lotions, toners and cosmetics. It's enough to make you rush out and head for the nearest supermarket, where at least you know what you need. I used to be seduced into buying bunches of lipsticks, eye colours and cosmetics that I didn't need or really want until I got my make-up drawer better organized.

Here is a check list of the basic essential tools you need to simplify your make-up and cut down on the time it takes. I have pared myself down to these, and although I couldn't do without any of them, I don't want to add to them either.

Two shades of liquid make-up base and one small empty bottle. You can mix your own colour to match your skin tone as your face changes colour with the seasons. During the summer you will need one quite dark base, and for those cold January days when your skin has that washed-out look you will need a light one. These can be mixed in the empty bottle, in small amounts to get the exact shade you want – which incidentally should never be more than two shades lighter or darker than your own skin tone.

One box of translucent powder, the lightest shade and texture possible, and two clean powder puffs – wash them often or buy more. Powder puffs must be scrupulously clean, or all the dedicated attention you have given to keeping your face as clean as possible is wasted.

Two cream blushers, one pinkish and one brownish, for shading and colouring.

Two powder blushers, again a light shade for day and a deeper shade for evening.

A pot of dark brown eyeshadow. (Not light green, powder blue or turquoise – they're horribly dated.) Carefully applied with your brush, the brown can be as light or as dark as you want.

Three eyebrow pencils, black, brown and auburn. You will use them all, whatever your colouring. And one pencil sharpener.

One lipstick brush.

Two eye brushes, one for powdered eyeshadow and one for cream shadow. These can be bought fairly inexpensively at your local art shop. The sable brushes are preferable: you can't lose them because they're long and they last for ever. The ones sold for make-up are always too short to use correctly. All film, photographic and TV make-up artists use proper paint brushes for their work.

One box of eyeshadow powders in the colours you prefer. Most cosmetic companies bring out little boxes which have a colour coordinated range for all skin colours, and they contain from three to ten colours depending on the brand. Experimenting with them is much more fun than finger painting!

One mascara wand, black or brown whatever your colouring. Never use blue or green or any of the gimmicks the cosmetic companies are constantly bringing out – they always look hard and fancy-dresslike.

No more than three or four lipsticks or lip glosses. No one changes their lipstick colour that often, and all those lipsticks you've been talked into buying at the make-up counters are just cluttering up your drawers and gathering dust, causing you to waste time looking for the right one. I suggest one deep glowing red for night and parties, one brownish-pink and one light pink (but not the shocking pink that was popular in the Sixties). Lipsticks today should have a translucent effect: use lip gloss alone or on top.

Finally, one covering pencil or stick to cover up the odd spot, freckle or blemish, or put under your eyes if the late nights have caught up with you.

And that's it. Precise as a doctor's bag. No frills, just the basic essentials for a perfect and *fast* make-up.

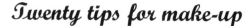

Twenty tips for make-up

1. If you want a healthy look, use brownish blusher on your cheekbones and in the centre of your forehead, under the chin and at the edges of your hairline. Blend carefully so there are no 'tide marks'.

2. To minimize a double chin, use shading blusher all around the jawbone, gradually fading colour under the jawline. Then apply a slightly darker shade directly under the chin and blend.

3. If you have odds and ends of old lipsticks cluttering your make-up table, squeeze them all together in a tiny pot. Apply with a lipbrush and you will have some fascinating new colours.

4. If eyelashes look clumpy when mascara is applied, separate them with another mascara wand, clean and damp.

5. A great way to get really thick looking lashes is to apply mascara under the hair drier. The hot air dries it very fast, so you can apply several coats in succession.

6. Mascara brushed gently on to the eyebrows looks very natural, but needs a steady hand.

7. When using eyeshadows and blushers don't forget that the darker colours of shading minimize your bad points and the lighter colours accentuate your good points. So subtle contouring can be done using the light and shade principle.

8. If you run out of lip gloss use Vaseline; if you run out of face powder use talcum or baby powder; and if you run out of blusher blend your lipstick in the palm of your hand with a little cold cream.

9. Always take your foundation and base down to your neck and throat and over the ears — if you don't you will have a different coloured face and neck, which looks very odd.

10. A child's pencil sharpener is the best thing for keeping all your make-up pencils sharp as a needle. Only then will you get the clearest and most effective results.

11. If you are in a hurry and have no time to take off your make-up and start again, try this. Blot your face thoroughly with tissues until all excess oil is absorbed, then gently re-apply a touch of base to the patchy areas around your nose and cheeks and chin. Powder

thoroughly and re-apply lip and eye make-up. You will have an instant new 'you' in less than two minutes.

12. Did you know you can get a free make-up at many cosmetic counters in the large department stores? It's great for that special evening.

13. Your body is composed of 60 per cent water, and it loves to be given more. After making up, splash water on to set the make-up (Evian spray is excellent).

14. Always carry blusher, it's the best quick make-up rejuvenator there is. A little colour splashed on, and *voilà* — instant glow and a look of 8 hours' sleep.

15. Teenagers have rediscovered that anathema of fifteen years ago — false eyelashes! This probably means they will be back in fashion soon.

Perfectly applied, false eyelashes can look quite dazzling for important evenings. Here are a few tips to make them look natural: never wear them more than a millimetre longer than your own lashes; mascara them as you would your own, top and bottom; if they go straight and floppy wash them with soap and water and roll them around a pencil wrapped in a tissue — next day they will be as good as new.

16. Don't try to change your natural skin tone. You were made a blonde, brunette or redhead, and extreme shades of basic foundation will look harsh and artificial.

17. Never use stark white highlighter under your brows or any other area. Try very pale pink or subtle greys and browns. Eyeshadow should emphasize your *eyes*, not your brand of eyeshadow.

18. Never use very pale lipstick. This was all the rage in the Sixties, so if you were too, forget them and try the see-through lip glosses. And use deeper tones.

19. Don't overdo blusher. It's supposed to make you look healthy, not as if you have a high fever. Always check your application with a hand mirror in profile before completing your make-up.

20. Remember that make-up should be fun. Experiment by all means, but when you take your 5 or 20 minutes to do your face — enjoy it! For me it's my best time for plotting and planning and day-dreaming, and my dressing table is my own little private island where I can get away from it all even if only for a few minutes.

Special effects for eyes

Eyes are your most fascinating feature to make up; given a little emphasis they can take on mystery or even different shapes, as you wish.

On the following pages the different eye shapes are illustrated. Find yours, and read the description that accompanies it. You will see that various depths of shading are called for – light, medium or deep. Follow these guidelines with any colour shadow you like, and remember to blend carefully for a natural look. (In many cases the entire eye is not made up; the shadow applications shown give you the basics only.)

Some normal eye shapes and different make-ups. Techniques for make-up are on the following pages.

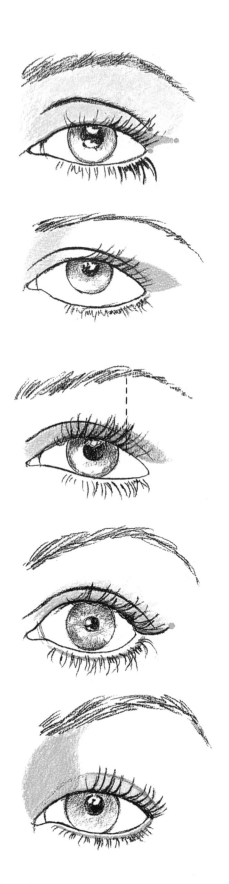

Close-set eyes *The emphasis should be on the outer corner of the eye. Apply a dark-toned shadow on the outer half, a light one on the inner half. Extend dark shadow slightly at outer corner and concentrate mascara here.*

Sloe eyes *Apply a deep-toned shadow to the outermost part of the lid, extending it slightly. Apply a light-toned shadow on inner corner and extend it to browbone. Apply mascara all over, on top and bottom lashes.*

Droopy eyes *Pencil a line close to upper lashes. Do not pencil outer edge of lid where the eye begins to droop. At this point, lift up the corner by pencilling up and out. Apply no shadow or mascara to the drooping outer corner. Use medium-toned shadow in area shown on sketch and stop mascara application at dotted line.*

Round eyes *Apply pencil close to lashes on upper lid. Make a dot at outer edge where last lash hits browbone. Extend liner to this point, smudge and blend well. Pencil under bottom lashes.*

Wide-set eyes *Accentuate inner corner with darker shadow, starting close to your nose. Shadow on outer corner should be lighter. Put more mascara on inner corner.*

Perfume

The ultimate turn-on

Fragrance is a tremendously personal thing. Scent should be your signature. On some women Chanel No. 5 smells divine: it lingers for hours on their skin, and all who come into contact with it get the message. On another woman the same perfume evaporates almost as soon as it touches her. You can only find the right perfume for your skin by experimenting.

Smell is probably the most basic of the senses; it conveys more emotionally potent messages than either sight or sound. Perfume is a powerful aphrodisiac to many men, and indeed the reason it is worn is not usually to benefit the wearer but to please others, especially those of the opposite sex. Women too are often turned on by a man who smells good, even if it's just subtle aftershave. The link between smell and sex is a primeval one, and there are many perfumes on the market designed to stimulate sexual interest. One of the most effective components is musk, which is chemically related to a male sex hormone, so this usually has a provocative effect.

But today the art of smelling wonderful is not just a dab of scent on the neck and wrists. There are many different versions and ways of using it. For the maximum effect try using several different products, all of which have the same basic scent. Perfumed bath oil is one of the best ways to ensure that every part of you smells great. Many of the perfume houses bring out bath oil to match their perfume: a few drops in the bath water go a long way. Matching shampoo, soap, colognes and talcum powder add to the effect. A good splash of your favourite cologne or toilet water applied liberally while your body is still damp from the bath is another way to maximize the fragrance impact. Since good perfume is expensive, using coordinated oils, powders and colognes makes sure that the precious essence is not wasted.

Perfume is the fastest and oldest way of getting your message across. But receiving the message is an imprecise art. What is sultry to one nose may be cloying to another. If you like your fragrance as much as you like the way you look, and it reflects how you feel, it's going to accentuate the image you have of yourself. Here are some terrific perfumes, and a message each might say about you.

Innocent   White Shoulders by Evyan. A famous perfume that suggests luxury. It is richly textured and contains mainly flower essences.

Classic   Chanel No. 5 by Chanel was the first 'modern' floral blend, vivacious and challenging. It has enduring appeal: thousands of women used it first as young girls, and have never used anything else. One of the great perfumes.

Modern   Opium by Yves Saint Laurent. A perfume made of light Oriental oils for today's woman. It has gorgeous packaging too.

Subtle   Jean Patou's Joy. This scent is like a silver spoon – some women were born to have it, many have always wanted it but can't afford it. Not overpowering, just Joy-ful and elegant.

Exciting   Rive Gauche by Yves Saint Laurent. Bright, reckless, exciting – with a more sensuous message that lingers on for an amazingly long time.

Sophisticated   Jean Deprez's Bal à Versailles has an Oriental accent. It is very strong, very sexy, very long-lasting, very distinctive, very expensive and my particular favourite.

Alluring   Fidji by Guy Laroche. A subtle blend of many essences, jasmine, sandalwood and myrrh. It adds up to a lot of impact, and is sophisticated and sexy in a subtle way. It is known for its staying power.

Scintillating   Jungle Gardenia by Tuvache. This is one of my favourites – heavy and musky, with a definite throb of the jungle drums creeping through the scent of gardenias! It is only made in the United States, but other brands of gardenia scents may be found in Britain.

Sexy   Shalimar by Guerlain. This may be too strong for most people. It is a knock-out, heavy, almost overpowering perfume that lingers for hours and has 'Wow' appeal to men, women, babies and dogs!

Demure   Miss Dior by Dior. A sweet, subtle, light smell – almost girlish but very appealing.

Powerful   Zibeline by Weil (also known as Secret of Venus). This perfume, which also comes in a very powerful bath oil, is not for the timid. It is musky, heavy and strong and with the bath oil lasts for hours on your skin. A scent that makes people constantly ask 'What are you wearing?'

Perfume should be applied at the pulse spots of throat, neck, wrists and elbows. It usually lasts from one to four hours depending on skin type.

Learn to layer scent, as you would build up tones and shades for a subtle make-up. Begin in the bath with perfumed soap and bath oil, then afterwards use scented dusting powder and body lotion. Spray on cologne, then follow that with the perfume itself.

Spray the hem of your skirt with perfume; rinse your tights in scented water.

Protect perfume from heat and sunlight as you would fine wine — both will die in the bottle otherwise.

Think of fragrance as you do lipstick: re-apply both from time to time. Usually after four hours the fragrance will have gone, even if you don't notice. Carry a perfume spray with you.

Keep old perfume bottles in drawers with scarves and undies; it is like having a potpourri in there.

Spray a little perfume in the basin when your pillow cases are being washed or on the ironing board before they are ironed.

Wear perfume to bed!

Apply foundation gently on to the face and neck, taking care to pull the skin as little as possible. Apply cream blusher.

With your sable eyeshadow brush apply brown shadow on the eyelid and below the bottom lashes.

With a clean powder puff, powder entire face including eyelashes and then brush lightly to remove excess.

Using the large sable blusher brush, redefine lightly the cheekbone area and forehead.

Carefully define the outline of the lips with auburn eyebrow pencil.

With the lipbrush paint the entire mouth, taking care not to go over the auburn outline.

Take an eyebrow pencil and with small brushlike strokes make the eyebrow into a gentle arch which complements your eye shape.

Using your black or brown mascara wand, apply mascara to the top and bottom lashes and apply eye liner at base of eyelashes on top lid.

With your sable eyeshadow brush gently stroke preferred colour over and under the eye, blending with your finger if necessary.

So there you are. The whole process shouldn't take more than 8 to 10 minutes when you have it down pat.

A fresh, young, but sophisticated outdoor look.

A sophisticated evening look, with emphasis drawn to the eyes by the subtle application of shadow and the clean-cut hair line.

These beautiful blue eyes and natural blond curly hair are the epitome of the pre-Raphaelite look, with a lack of emphasis on eye make-up.

An elegant look for redheads, again with emphasis on shading on the upper eyelid and the cheeks.

Hairstyles

Beautifully conditioned hair, freshly washed, well cut – utter simplicity.

A very vampy look for a very sophisticated lady.

*980 version of the 1960s
geometric cut.*

*Plaits are fashionable
again and shown to great
advantage in this style*

Hair

The quality, texture and type of your hair determines what you can do with it and what styles you can wear.

Hair is probably the bane of most women's lives (it is certainly mine), and it accounts for their biggest expenditure in time and money. Absolutely everyone seems dissatisfied with her natural hair – straight-haired girls want to be curly; curly-headed ones crave straight, shining locks; those with thick hair want it to be fine, those with fine want it to be thick. The only solution to hair woes is to accept your hair for what it is, understand it with all its limitations and problems, and never try to force it into a contrived style that won't work and causes you aggravation through being too complicated to do at home.

But whatever type of hair you have, the condition of it depends, as does most of your beauty, on what you eat. I've said it before and I'll say it again and again, *nothing* beats correct nutrition and diet for glowing health and beauty of skin and hair.

Hair is one of today's most important accessories. If your hair looks good, you look good. Most women want versatile hair, hair that they can change at night or to suit their mood. This demands that it should have a certain amount of length, at least below the chin, so that it can be pulled back or put up. The quickest way to dress up hair is to tie a ribbon round your head, or put in combs, or twist up either all or part of the hair.

But always try to keep it simple and not contrived-looking. You don't want to spend loads of time and money on upkeep – nobody has the time (or inclination) to sit in the hairdressers three times a week unless she is a professional model or an actress. Very few of us even have the time for once a month.

What you need is a style versatile, quick and easy enough to do yourself, one that will always look good whatever the weather and whatever your activity, be it housework, office work, disco or exercising. The more aware you are of your hair type, the better you will be able to deal with it in terms of styling and setting. So find out what kind of hair yours is, and learn to make the best of it.

Fine hair

This is usually thin and limp, gets dirty and greasy easily, and needs frequent shampooing to help it look good and full. It lacks body and looks best with a blunt cut.

Fine hair needs very careful handling, as it has a tendency to brittleness and can break easily. Perms are usually a disaster for this kind of hair, as they dry it up tremendously and the hair can get so dry that it snaps off. I know: I have fine hair, and I had a perm recently which, although I liked at first, I regret to this day. My hair has still not completely recovered.

Medium hair

This is the ideal hair in every way. It can adapt to practically any kind of style or length. It does not need too much shampooing, it holds a set for several days, and looks good hanging free or loose. It can take a blunt or a layered cut equally well. Oh, lucky people with this kind of hair!

Coarse hair

Coarse hair looks best with a blunt cut, medium to long length. If it is too long it will become weighed down and thus lose its set. If it is too short it may have a tendency to stick out or look bushy and unkempt.

Curly hair

How I envy those with curly hair, especially thick wavy curls. Curly hair looks best when it is short or medium length and beautifully cut, and allowed to do its own thing. Some women find however that if they allow their curly hair to do its own thing it becomes a frizzy mess, so they have it straightened. This can be done very well but it has a tendency to weaken the hair, so be sure you go to a reputable salon. Hot weather, humidity and rain always makes curly hair curlier.

Two variations on a classic style for long, straight, fine hair. The chignon style is good for accentuating high cheek bones and also a boon for those with busy lives as it takes a minimum of time. The other style needs more care and very clean hair as it must flow and not look lank or greasy.

Overleaf (left): Day and gala evening look for thick curly hair. Sophisticated yet simple.
(Right): Day and evening looks for fine blond hair involving a good cut and a minimum of setting and care.

What is hair?

The hair you can see is actually dead matter. It is the hair follicles under the scalp that are living and active and growing and pushing out each individual hair.

Hair is constantly replacing itself from the follicles, but with no particular pattern of growth. It grows faster in the warm summer months and often becomes thinner and more brittle in the winter. Hair grows at the approximate rate of half an inch a month or 6 inches a year. You lose on average between 50 to 100 hairs a day from your scalp, so don't despair if you see a hairbrush full of your crowning glory – this is the natural process of renewal.

Unless your hair is trimmed regularly you are likely to get split ends. This is a condition in which the last inch or so of the hair, which is also the oldest, becomes weakened and literally divides into two or three sections. These should be cut off or they will split further and further up the hair shaft, which is unhealthy and makes the hair look ragged.

Pregnancy has a marked effect on the hair because of the enormous hormonal changes the body undergoes. It is essential to take the right kind of food and vitamins while pregnant, to prevent hair loss after the baby is born.

Hair is 95 per cent protein so to keep it in good health you need lots of the following: fish, chicken and turkey, milk and cheese, nuts and wholegrain breads and cereals.

You can make a good protein drink by mixing the juice of parsley, carrot, celery and spinach. These vegetables are particularly beneficial to the glossiness of your hair.

Supplements for hair beauty
B vitamins (especially pantothenic acid – essential for beautiful hair)
Brewers' yeast tablets
Wheatgerm
Iron
6 glasses of water a day

Do-it-yourself hair treatments

For smoothing out frizzy hair
This is a very old recipe. It doesn't straighten the hair, but it does smooth down the scales of the hair shaft, making the hair shinier and more manageable.

Make a thin paste (the consistency of cake batter) from a cup of flour and approximately two-thirds of a cup of cold water. Mix until all lumps have disappeared. Apply to dry, unwashed hair, smoothing the hair straight back. Leave for 20 minutes then rinse thoroughly. It will take about 5 minutes to rinse all the flour out. Now shampoo hair once with very mild shampoo.

A treatment to get rid of dandruff

Boil 4 tablespoons of thyme in 2 cups of water for 10 minutes. Strain and cool. Pour one cup over damp, shampooed hair, making sure the liquid covers the scalp. Massage gently. Do not rinse off, but dry hair as normal. This recipe makes enough for two treatments.

A conditioner for very dry hair

Warm 2 tablespoons of olive oil. Massage thoroughly into the hair and scalp. Wrap a very hot damp towel around the head for 20 minutes, and then shampoo twice. This will give a shiny gloss to the hair.

Shampooing

Before you shampoo, always comb your hair to separate snarls and tangles and to get rid of some of the dirt and hair spray. Never try to pull snarls with a brush or comb when the hair is wet, as this will cause breakage. Hair is slightly elastic and stretches when it is wet, so that when it dries it can snap like a twig.

To get the best results invest in a shower attachment from the chemist or hardware store (the plastic ones are quite cheap, and last for ages). This ensures thorough rinsing off of all the shampoo and makes the whole process much easier.

Different types of hair need different shampooing techniques.

Fine hair

Fine hair needs to be washed at least twice a week to keep it looking fresh and full. It is best to alternate types of shampoo, using a conditioning shampoo one day and a mild one the next.

The hair should be completely wetted with warm, never hot, water and then a small amount of shampoo, just enough to raise a lather, should be worked methodically into the scalp and hair for about 30 seconds. Shampoo only once, then rinse thoroughly. Most instructions on shampoos recommend two applications, but I believe firmly that too much washing robs hair of its natural oils. Provided you wash your hair really thoroughly, one lot of shampoo is just as efficient as two.

Once a week apply conditioner to the ends only. Too much conditioner on dry fine hair tends to make it unmanageable.

Medium hair
This hair can go for up to eight days without looking as if it needs washing. But you (or your beloved) are the best judge of that, since hair should smell good as well as looking good. It may need more frequent shampooing, especially if you smoke or are around people who smoke: smoke smells have a nasty habit of lingering in the locks.

Medium hair can take two washes and a lot of rinsing with lukewarm water. Use conditioner as necessary.

Oily hair
Although this is the type of hair that needs washing the most, it is best not to do so too often as this stimulates the surface of the scalp to produce even more oil.

Shampoo once or twice, trying not to rotate the scalp too much. Do not use a cream rinse or conditioner on oily hair and try to cut down on the amount of fatty and fried food you eat, as this will cause less oil to be manufactured in the sebaceous glands.

Never use ordinary soap or detergent on any type of hair, as this leaves a dull film which makes the hair lank and lifeless for weeks.

Conditioning and colouring

How to condition hair
Conditioners are to your hair as moisturizers are to your skin. Regular conditioning is essential if you do any of the following to your hair: tinting, perming, streaking or using heated rollers and blow driers.

There are basically two kinds of conditioners: the heavy, deeply penetrating type which should only be used every three or four weeks, and the instant conditioner that you can use after every shampoo. If your hair is tinted or permed, however, you remove some of the colour and perm every time you condition, so you shouldn't use conditioner more than once every two or three weeks.

Apply conditioner and comb through hair thoroughly, paying particular attention to the ends as these are the oldest, driest and brittlest part of your hair. Hair that is shoulder length or more can be as old as 6 or 8 years, and needs extra special care at all times.

Hair colouring

The most radical way to change your look is to change your hair colouring.

I strongly believe that a professional hair colourist is the best person to colour your hair. There are a million brands of do-it-yourself colouring dye and tint sets on the chemists' shelves, but if you plan to colour or rinse for the first time I advise a professional job. In this way you will get the best advice about what you should use on your particular type of hair, before you attempt an at-home method. Don't be afraid to ask questions; most hairdressers like to chat.

Electrical appliances for the hair

There are dozens of electrical bits and pieces in the stores for your hair – sometimes you just don't know what to try or what will work for you. There is one thing to remember when using any of them: heat is the greatest enemy of hair, and the dry heat that comes from these appliances is the worst of all for drying, breaking and weakening hair.

When you're under the drier at the hairdresser, always set the control to medium or low, *never* hot. However much of a hurry everyone is in, don't stay under the drier a second longer than necessary. The same thing applies to blow driers. Don't use on 'hot', don't get the drier too close to your hair, and never let the heat from the drier blow directly on to your face and skin.

The best way to dry hair is naturally, but of course this isn't always quick or efficient enough. Do try always to blot off as much excess water as possible with a towel; this will necessitate less time under the drier.

Wigs

I think every woman should have a wig or a hairpiece, for a special occasion or to whip on when something important occurs and you 'can't do a thing with your hair', or just for a change, to alter your look or image for a while. You may get tired of the same old you staring back out of the mirror every morning – I know I do sometimes – and nothing changes your appearance more completely than a wig.

The best wigs today are of man-made fibres and are as easy to take care of as drip-dry shirts. They are usually made of kanekelon or nylon, and stitched on to a wide mesh which pops over your head like a cap. With the help of a couple of hairpins the wig will remain firmly in place through hail, wind and even lovemaking (perhaps a few extra grips for this activity), until you take it off.

These wigs blossom with rough treatment. You do not need to treat them with tender loving care – in fact the more they are washed, brushed, back-combed and sprayed, the more natural looking they become. I keep mine scrunched up in a drawer with my scarves and Katyana, my eight year old, uses them when she's playing dressing-up games with her friends. Stuff one inside-out in the corner of your suitcase on a trip abroad and you have an instant lift to your appearance in a matter of minutes.

Some people, either through illness or for cosmetic reasons, have to wear a wig all the time, but I do not advise wearing one often unless you have to because it can make the scalp perspire too much, and weaken your own hair by clogging the hair follicles.

Falls or hair pieces should ideally be made of real hair by a proper wigmaker, and should resemble as closely as possible the colour, texture and length of your own hair. They are particularly useful for those with fine hair, as they can fill out the hair at the back where it is usually most needed.

How to put on a wig
Holding the wig at the front and keeping it upside down, brush it through thoroughly. Then pull the wig on from the front to the back, making sure that the centre of the front is aligned to your own hairline. Make certain none of your own hair has escaped and then secure the wig with hairgrips. Arrange in the desired style with a brush, lightly back-combing if necessary.

Tips for hair-lovers

Don't wash your hair more than three or four times a week or it will lose its natural oils.

Almond oil and olive oil are great conditioners for the hair. Once a week rub oil thoroughly all over your hair and scalp and leave on overnight. Cover your head with a cotton scarf while you sleep, or the pillow case will be a disaster area. If you or your man can't bear the smell, use an ordinary conditioner instead. Wash as normal in the morning and your hair will look healthy and gorgeous.

Put lemon juice on fair hair in the sun and your hair will become blonder and blonder.

Always keep dark or tinted hair covered with a hat or a scarf while sunning and swimming, otherwise it will lighten up considerably. If you use a blond tint, it can even turn green with too much sun!

Never use rollers with brushes in them on wet hair; these break the hair, and may also get caught which can cause complete disaster.

Always put tissues over heated rollers as the spikes can break the hair.

Don't always use the same shampoo. Hair becomes accustomed to one type and does not respond as well as it should. Change brands every two or three months.

Rinse hair again and again with cool water, even when you feel you've rinsed enough. When your hair squeaks you know all the shampoo is out.

Excessive brushing strains the hair and can cause it to break and fall out. Get the tangles out gently with a comb but leave the heavy brushing for your dog. Only if you have very thick hair should you brush it often.

It doesn't matter how good and healthy your hair is, a perm definitely damages it. If you must have a perm, use the lightest and gentlest you can get, and don't have it done more than once a year.

If you tint your hair don't go more than a few shades either lighter or darker than your own skin tones or it will look unnatural.

It is normal for scalp and hair condition to change seasonally. In summer it is quite common for the scalp

to be oily and the hair dry. If that is the case, use a shampoo for oily hair on your scalp and a conditioner on the ends of your hair only. For a dry scalp and oily hair, use conditioner on your scalp first then use an 'oily' shampoo, but don't massage it too vigorously near your scalp.

Always comb wet hair at the ends first, and then work upwards. Never start at the scalp.

Lemon juice rinse is one of the oldest hair treatments around, but it's still one of the best. Use regularly to give supershine to all hair types. Squeeze and strain the juice of half a lemon into a cup of cool water and stir. Pour over damp hair, leave for 3 minutes, then rinse with warm water.

Always use natural fibre brushes on your hair — bristle is much better than scratchy nylon, and wire or metal brushes and combs are the worst.

One heaped tablespoon a day of non-fermenting brewers' yeast, which is a natural protein rich in B vitamins, sprinkled on cereal or mixed with yoghurt, soup or fruit juice is all you need to give your diet a supplement of the vitamins and protein necessary for your hair. Most health food stores have a wide variety of non-fermenting nutritional yeast to choose from.

To make a camomile rinse for blond hair, put 10 tea bags of camomile tea in a quart of water and boil for 10 minutes. Let this cool, then pour over damp, rinsed hair after your shampoo. Do not rinse again. This makes enough for four rinses.

If you are colouring your hair yourself always test a small strand of hair first before you do the whole head. This is the only way of checking that the colour looks right on you.

Never colour and perm your hair at the same time, as the different chemical processes can cause lasting damage. Always leave at least a month between the two.

A good haircut is the fastest, most dramatic way to a 'new you'.

Finally, always follow *absolutely* the instructions on all colours, conditioners and home perms. If they say leave on for 5 minutes, don't leave on for 7 — especially in the case of colour or a perm.

*Right: A classic look made
elegantly formal by the
arrangement of flowers in
the chignon. Flowers are an
instant dressing-up
accessory to any hairstyle,
long or short, up or down –
as are slides, combs,
ribbons and plaits.*

*Right: Instant glamour
without tears. Long,
medium-thick hair is coiled
and pinned to the side of
the head for a striking
evening look.*

*Left: This style is perfect
for baby-fine hair. A lot
depends on the cut and
condition as there is
basically very little styling.*

Right: This style works equally well with thick, medium or fine hair. It is classic yet modern and young and looks good with a variety of modern outfits. But it must have either curly hair or a perm for it to have staying power.

Left: You have to have classic and regular features and fairly thick hair to look good in this style. But it is quite stunning when worn by the right person. Think twice before you commit yourself as it will take two months to grow out!

Left: An easy, pretty look for short curly or permed hair. It goes well with day or evening styles, suits young and old and is practicable for all face shapes.

Caring for the Rest of You

Hands

The hands are the recipients of more abuse, more strain and more wear and tear than practically any other part of the body except for the feet. Since our hands are on show in their naked glory most of the time, it behoves us to give them special care. They are also a sure indication of age. The skin on the back of the hands is very thin and there is nothing to plump it up with, so once it starts to go, it goes fast. You've seen the woman with a young face and figure who could be thirty until you look at her wrinkled, puffy and liver-spotted hands and realize she's much older.

Always keep a bottle of moisturizer hand lotion (the easy to apply plunger-type) in your bathroom, next to the kitchen sink, near the washing machine or anywhere your hands are getting wet and chapped or doing hard labour. *Always* wear rubber gloves when doing housework, washing up, any hard domestic tasks or gardening. Use moisturizer or barrier cream underneath the gloves.

Two useful tips
To whiten hands that have got that dingy, grey, end-of-winter look, cut a lemon in half and rub gently over the back of the hands.

If your hands are very chapped from rough work or gardening, soak them in a solution of warm milk for 10 minutes. Repeat once or twice a week until they are better.

Nails

Nails need constant care and attention. Too much sun or extreme cold makes nails dry and brittle (so does the chlorine in swimming pools). Nails, like hair, are dead matter: the part that you see is no longer growing. Because of this they cannot heal if you break or chip them, so keeping a coat of varnish, coloured or colourless, on all the time is an excellent protection. Detergents and household cleaners wreak havoc with nails, hence the importance of wearing rubber gloves. Never use nail clippers or scissors to cut nails, as this can make them break and split. Always use an emery board, *never* a steel nail file. Bad, bad, bad!

Nails grow about a quarter of an inch a month: it takes approximately six months to grow a normal length nail.

Manicure

The tools you need for a do-it-yourself manicure (gather them first to save time):

Emery boards	Hand lotion
Cuticle remover	Nail brush
Orange sticks	Small bowl of soapy water
Cotton wool	(use mild shampoo)
Oily nail varnish remover	Cuticle clippers
(never use acetone – it's	Nail polish and base coat
terribly drying)	

Remove old nail varnish with cotton wool.
Soak nails in bowl of soapy water.
Remove dirt from behind nails with brush.
Dry nails, and apply cuticle remover to each nail.
Using orange stick, gently push cuticle back as far as
possible to reveal the half moon at the base of nail.
If necessary remove any dried skin or hangnails with
small cuticle clippers.
Shape nails to a smooth natural curve with emery
board. File from the side of the nail to the centre. Do
not use emery board like a saw, backwards and
forwards, as this can split nails.
Apply hand cream and massage thoroughly.
Dip cotton wool in water and wipe off all traces of
cream from nails.
Apply base coat of varnish in smooth strokes. This
protects nails, makes coloured polish last longer, and
fills in any tiny ridges that there may be on the nails.
Apply coloured polish in three strokes, the first down
the centre of the nail and then one on each side. Make
sure you take smooth, firm strokes, not wobbly ones.
Wait until thoroughly dry (always use quick-drying
polish — it saves time) and apply a second coat of
varnish the same as before. If you really want it to last
a long time apply a third coat.
After polish has dried, apply a protective top coat of
colourless varnish.

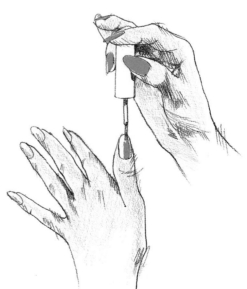

Pedicure

What you will need:
Shallow basin or pan of
soapy water
Cotton wool or cotton-
wool pads
Oily polish remover
Orange sticks
Hand lotion

Towel and facial tissues
Emery boards
Pumice stone
Cuticle remover
Nail clippers
Nail scissors
Nail polish and base coat

Remove old polish.
Soak feet in the pan of soapy water (this may be
shampoo or *mild* detergent) for 5 minutes.
Use pumice stone or callus remover on rough spots
like the back of your heels and the pads of your big
toes. Also remove dry hardened skin on the soles of
the feet.
Dry feet on a towel and apply cuticle remover
over nails; massage it in.
Push back the cuticles with an orange stick.
Clip off dead cuticles with cuticle cutters. You must be
very careful doing this as you can clip too
enthusiastically and draw blood.
If your toenails are hard, cut them gently with small
nail scissors. Make sure you cut them absolutely
straight across, as if you cut into the sides it
encourages ingrowing toenails, which can be very
painful. If nails are not too hard, use an emery board to
file them to the required length. It is always best to
keep toenails as short as possible. They look better,
and they won't ladder your stockings!
Massage the feet with hand lotion, paying special
attention to heels and soles.
Wipe excess cream off toes and dry. Fold up a tissue
and arrange like a concertina between the toes to
separate them and prevent them smudging each other.
Apply base coat, polish and top coat as with manicure.
Don't put on shoes and stockings for at least three-
quarters of an hour or all your good work will be
undone.

Teeth

The best beauty care for teeth is prevention. Once the rot sets in there is not much you can do except keep at bay all the known decay-makers.

Care of the teeth must begin in infancy, with a good diet. Nutritional standards in the West are declining rapidly, and very young children are bearing the brunt of this. It is a horrifying fact that in Britain 3 out of 10 people over the age of sixteen have some false teeth. And this figure increases rapidly with age.

It is the combination of correct diet and correct brushing that is the key to healthy teeth. Brushing your teeth will not *prevent* decay, just as cleaning your floors and windows regularly will not prevent your house falling down if it has structural problems.

Correct brushing can however deal with the substance called plaque, a coated build-up on the teeth. Plaque is one of the main causes of decay, and also of gum disease which is a major factor in all teeth problems. Although plaque can be removed with regular, scrupulous brushing you should visit the dentist regularly to have a proper scaling, which also removes any tartar, or calcified plaque.

Plaque thrives on sweet things and all sugar and white flour products, so obviously less of these means less plaque. If you *must* eat sweets, instead of nibbling them throughout the day, eat them all at the same time and then brush, brush, brush!

Correct brushing

Most people brush their front teeth scrupulously and then forget about the rest. And they brush only their teeth instead of their teeth and gums. Gums are the support of the teeth and must be cared for just as thoroughly.

Choose the correct kind of toothbrush. Most dentists agree that a soft brush is best, and it should be small so that it reaches into the crevices and into every corner of your mouth. Round-tipped bristle brushes are recommended because nylon ones can scratch teeth and gums.

As soon as your brush begins to lose its shape, throw it away. However well you rinse and care for them, most brushes have lost their efficiency by the end of two or three months.

Most of us brush our teeth incorrectly. We use long, violent, horizontal strokes that damage the gums and don't get to the hidden areas where the plaque collects. The important thing is to concentrate on cleaning not only the teeth, but also the crevices between them. The most dangerous plaque forms near to and under the gums, especially between the teeth. Plaque is very glue-like and it needs a lot of brushing to remove it thoroughly. Three minutes is the minimum time you should spend brushing.

Holding the brush at an angle of 45 degrees, brush with an up and down movement. First the front, top and bottom, and then the back teeth, top and bottom, paying particular attention to the *inside* of the back teeth.

The only way effectively to remove particles of food lodged in between teeth is to use dental floss. (In the United States no teeth cleaning process is now complete without using dental floss, and it is beginning to catch on in England.) Use it at least once a day, being careful not to be too diligent and cut through to your gums.

Freshen with a mouth wash or by rinsing with warm water.

Follow this procedure after breakfast, if possible after lunch (keep a toothbrush at the office – why not?) and before bedtime and you will take a major step towards beautiful healthy teeth.

At the first sign of a toothache or bleeding gums or other problems, *see your dentist*. The longer a bad tooth condition exists the worse it will become.

Body hair

Body hair, a little or a lot, is common to all of us, men and women alike. But although it is a universal human characteristic, it is *not* universally admired. Many women spend a lot of time removing hair from their arms, legs and elsewhere.

Here are some of the most effective methods.

Epilaxia – hair removal by plucking
Use   For eyebrows only.
Pros   A quick, efficient way to shape eyebrows and control straggly growth.
Cons   It smarts, and ingrown hairs and 'missed' roots show up as little black dots unless tweezed in the direction of growth.
Tips   Go over eyebrows with astringent-soaked cotton wool before tweezing. This removes any oil, and helps you get a grip on tiny hairs. Use a strong magnifying mirror, slant-edged tweezers (clean them with alcohol before use). Brush the brows up into desired arch and pluck only those hairs that blur the line.

Waxing
Use   For legs, arms, underarms, body.
Pros   No ugly regrowth stubble, and no injury to skin or hair follicle. Waxing tends, in time, to weaken regrowth.
Cons   It's expensive, and it hurts (how much depends on the part of the body and your threshold of pain). There may be an untidy regrowth period before the hair is long enough to wax again.
Tips   Waxing works best if you allow longer between sessions than you would with other processes (more hair gives the wax better 'grip'), but if you start waxing in winter, growth will have been substantially reduced by next summer's bikini time. Waxing is most effective on legs and around the bikini area.

Electrolysis – use of electric current transmitted through a stainless-steel or platinum stylet inserted in a pore to render the hair follicle sterile

Use   Primarily on the face and sensitive parts of the body like the breasts and stomach.

Pros   Permanent removal of hair.

Cons   It is time-consuming: only a certain number of hairs can be removed at a session and many treatments may be needed to get rid of very strong follicles. It hurts (how much again depends on you – some women nap during treatment, others find it excruciating).

Tips   If you have the nerve, a steady hand and patience, there is a safe, moderately priced, battery-operated electrolysis tool for home use.

Depilation – destruction of hair by chemical breakdown Chemical depilatories are made in powder, cream or spray form. These dissolve the hair above and below the surface of the skin.

Use   On legs, arms, underarms, body and, in some cases, on the face, but be extremely careful here.

Pros   This is the least painful method and is very effective – regrowth stubble, possibilities of ingrown hairs or areas you might miss when shaving are all eliminated. Use of depilatories tends, in time, to weaken hair growth.

Cons   Because depilatories are strong enough to dissolve hair, they can be too strong for some skin types. (Attention fair and delicate skins!) A skin-patch test 24 hours before using for the first time is a must. Depilatories cannot be used on irritated or broken skin.

Tips   A depilatory takes longer than usual to work if you have been used to shaving. Test progress on a small area after a few minutes; unless hair comes off easily, wait a few minutes and test another patch. Lots of rinsing with cool water makes it easier, and always moisturize thoroughly afterwards.

Shaving – electric or manual razor

Use   For legs and underarms.

Pros   Quick, easy, inexpensive. It does not harm hair, nor does it stimulate regrowth as some people believe.

Cons   It dries up the skin. There is the chance of nicks and scrapes. Regrowth is rapid because the root is not removed or damaged by shaving (you have to do it often to prevent 5 o'clock shadow on your legs).

Tips Cuts and nicks are eliminated if you always use a clean sharp blade with proper shaving soap, not ordinary soap which increases razor drag. Rinse the razor after every stroke. Never use a dry razor on dry skin; hair absorbs water and becomes elastic, and is therefore easier to shave when wet.

Electric razors work better if you use special electric shaver conditioner. You get a closer shave by using short, pressing strokes rather than long, dragging ones. Electric razors are ideal for quick zips over the bikini line.

Shaving will not dry the skin providing you use the special shaving soap or electric-shave preparation already mentioned, rinse well after shaving, then use lavish amounts of moisturizing body lotions or creams. Try alternating safety and electric razors; many women find it easier on the skin.

Bleaching – a disguising process, not a removing one
Use On the face, forearms, body.
Pros For women with a small amount of hair this is an ideal method, especially for facial hair. There is no regrowth problem and touch-ups are simple to do.
Cons It takes time and close attention. A skin-patch test 24 hours before the first bleaching is essential. The hair must be completely stripped of colour, rather than bleached to a reddish-blond; this may require two bleaching sessions initially.
Tips Use a good quality, commercially prepared bleaching preparation and follow directions to the letter. Have a timer handy while you bleach. Dark hair may require two sessions, 24 hours apart, to be completely stripped of colour. (Two short sessions are better for your skin than one prolonged session.) Watch carefully for regrowth. Facial hair will probably need a weekly touch-up, but hair on forearms grows more slowly.

Clothes

We all have an image of ourselves which we present to the world in many different ways, but most of all perhaps in the way we dress.

Clothes reveal a great deal about a person. Each time you dress you are showing people how you feel about yourself. That chic smart secretary, that dowdy but expensively dressed matron, that teenager with the wild T-shirt saying he doesn't conform – they are all making a statement. I think most women would like to dress well and look smart and well groomed without having to go as far as imitating the chic Vogue model.

Here are some of my basic tips for making the best of what you have, and of what is available in the shops and reasonably priced. Shopping carefully is crucial today; clever women are looking at clothes more critically and with an eye to making them last, not just for one season but for years to come. Ask yourself these questions before you buy anything new.

Does it fit in with your present wardrobe without necessitating a lot of new bits and pieces to go with it?

Is it a fashion trend or just a fad? Fashion constantly evolves, and often it's hard to realize the difference between this genuine progression and a fad. Anything over-emphasized and a bit flashy can usually be construed as a fad. For example, very wide shoulders are a fad that is

141

high style now and will not last. But the general silhouette of clothes is changing gradually, and the emphasis of the wider shoulder is definitely part of the new silhouette. Skin-tight trousers are another fad, but again the new slimmer shape means that those old bell-bottoms are unfortunately and obviously out of date.

Does it match your lifestyle? It's no good buying a black velvet cocktail hat at a bargain price if the only party you go to is the annual bosses' bash at Christmas, nor do you want heavy walking brogues if the furthest out of London you get is St James's Park. If what you buy is not in character with your lifestyle its use will be limited and the expense unjustified.

If you live in jeans, it's better to buy more expensive and therefore better quality jeans that will justify the cost. If you pay a lot for something and wear it constantly, that is far more of a budget bargain than if you buy something cheaply and only wear it once.

Do you like it? You must always dress to please yourself. It is no good being persuaded by the blue-rinsed and intimidating saleslady that it 'looks wonderful on you dear, and this is the *in* thing this year.' If you yourself aren't happy in it, it will become another white elephant languishing at the back of your wardrobe. And you won't get your money's worth.

Finally, do you feel natural and at ease in it? If you feel even slightly self-conscious – if the hemline is a little too short for your taste, or the skirt split too high – *don't* buy.

The real secret of good dressing is to be individual and stylish enough to make a statement about yourself that is original, attractive and fun and yet not be so over the top that you are uncomfortable and inhibited. Your personality is projected through your clothes, but the consciousness of self must not become self-consciousness. If you feel that what you are wearing is not really attractive you may have a tendency to hide, and when this happens people react to you with a negative attitude. What you wear should always cause a positive reaction, especially in yourself. There is nothing better than a compliment to make you feel good, and with the right statement about yourself in your wardrobe those compliments could become a habit. Try and get that special feeling whenever you buy anything – the feeling for really looking great and feeling confident. *Never* buy anything you're only half-hearted about or think 'may come in useful one day'.

When you are shopping remember that 'just looking' is your right. Don't be intimidated by haughty or hostile salesladies: their merchandise is there for *you*, and you'd better make sure you are pleased with it before you put out your hard-earned money on it. If you have a friend whose opinion you really trust, take her with you. If you are confident enough of your own taste, go alone.

Shopping for the exact things you require needs careful planning. Make a list of what you need and of the shops where you are most likely to find them. Just remember you are a total original, your own work of art, and there is no one else who looks like you. Within the limitations of your budget you have the opportunity to wear the clothes that do most for you, and to tell the world that you are looking and feeling good.

Fashion passes, style remains. You should aim for taste and your individual style. Taste is more conservative, style needs more courage. One can have taste yet not have style – they are not the same – nor can one take style on and off like lipstick. Style is a visible and very personal aura, not to be confused with glamour. It is something you acquire, but it must be special to you and not copied slavishly from other women.

Here is an elementary list that is the foundation for a good wardrobe. It is wise to restrict yourself to a couple of basic colours at first, as this will give you a much more coordinated look. As an example I shall use brown and beige, which also blend well with a large range of subordinate colours.

The ideal wardrobe

Coats

A coat is the piece of clothing seen by more people than any other, and the most necessary and practical. If you can afford it I suggest two coats. One should be a tan or a beige raincoat type, loose enough to go over your jackets and shirts and bulky sweaters, and the second one a more classic style, perhaps a trench coat which is slightly fitted and can go over more dressy things.

Jackets

You will need two jackets. The baggy look is passé now, so they should be slightly fitted with some emphasis on the shoulders, since this is the present trend. Let's say one in burgundy velvet and the other in a tweedy fabric (one of the jackets should match a skirt).

Skirts

So that you may have a complete ensemble, I suggest one skirt in burgundy velvet, cut straight. The second one could be camel coloured and perhaps pleated, and the third a longer gathered skirt in an abstract print.

Trousers

Most of you have jeans so I'm not presuming that you have to invest in that most necessary item. (Whatever did we wear before jeans were invented?) I suggest also one pair of beige corduroy jeans or trousers, cut narrow enough so that they can be tucked into boots, and one pair of more dressy pants in either brown or tan gaberdine or wool. These should not be as tight as the corduroy and may have a slightly pleated effect – a touch of the Fred Astaires.

Shirts and blouses

Four or five if budget permits: two shirtwaist classic shirts in plain colours, e.g. brown and cream; one 'workman's-type' shirt in a light wool plaid mixture; one feminine ruffled blouse which is versatile enough to double for day or evening wear; and one perfectly plain shift type blouse.

Plain colours are best for blouses, as detail can be added with scarves, belts and jewellery.

Sweaters

Aim for four or five: two polo or cowl necks, depending on your proportions, one brown, one beige; one bulky heavy-duty sweater, such as a fisherman's knit in cream, which has buttons and can also double as a jacket; one schoolboy type V-neck which can be worn with the shirts for a classic look, or with a tie for a more businesslike look; and one sleeveless cardigan or waistcoat in a tweedy wool mixture.

On the following pages you can see examples of the clothes I have described. All of them come from my wardrobe but similar ones can be found in most fashion stores.

Dresses

Dresses are probably nowadays the hardest thing to shop for: the choice is so vast, the styles so diverse. What to go for and when to wear a dress at all is becoming a problem in our casual society.

144

Perhaps dresses are not for every woman today, and it is hard to advise all the different types of women on a basic design. But as a rough guideline, I would pick one sleek sweater-dress in a bright vibrant colour – red, burgundy or green – and two printed silk or challis dresses with full sleeves, scoop necks and fullish skirts. These can be dressed up or down according to the occasion.

Shoes and boots
You should have at least one pair of tan coloured medium-heeled boots; one pair of tan medium-heeled walking shoes, to wear for a sporty look; one pair of high-heeled court shoes in suede or brown leather; one pair of beige high-heeled sandals to wear for a dressier occasion.

Belts
Three or four belts in different colours, shapes and textures add tremendous versatility to an outfit. You could choose, for example, a thin brown lizard belt, a wide suede wraparound belt that can be tied, and a metallic gold or silver 'dressed-to-kill' ornamental belt.

Handbags
I am of the school of thought that believes accessories to be one of the most important parts of your wardrobe. I do intensely dislike cheap handbags. I realize it is not within most women's budgets to buy the more expensive bags, but in Italy and France a woman will forgo other luxuries to buy the best handbag she can afford.

As an investment it is first-rate, as a good leather handbag will last you for years and look better in the long run, whereas a cheap one will fall apart and rapidly end up looking scruffy, which does little for your overall look.

There are some very good inexpensive small pochettes or purses around which are useful, practical and make a change from your everyday look.

Jewellery
Jewellery is extremely personal. Very often we are forced to wear a particular piece of jewellery we don't even like that much (a wedding or engagement ring, Grandma's old brooch, a 21st birthday gift from Mum and Dad). But jewellery – the lack of it or a surfeit of it – can make or break an outfit.

For the purpose of this book, I am talking about fake jewellery. And as you know the counters of department stores are overflowing these days with glorious gilts, huge simulated pearls and sparkling silver imitations.

Gold is definitely a winner with the basic colour scheme of brown, tan and beige (as with most), so here's what I suggest you get.

One pair of gold hoop earrings, the size depending on the shape of your face and your degree of flamboyance

One pair of gold 'stud' earrings

One pair of pearl studs

One gold choker – the kind that clings to the neck

A selection of gold and ivory (plastic) bangles to wear individually or together

Two or three strings of graduated pearls. You may feel that pearls are very dated, but with the pared-down look of today's clothes they make a definite statement

One gold and diamante brooch, perhaps in the shape of a butterfly or star

Two or three gilt chains, which again can be worn singly or together

Summer extras

For those of you optimistic enough to invest in a summer wardrobe for this chilly climate I recommend the following fundamental items to work in with your existing garments.

I like a lot of white in the summer. True it gets dirty quickly, but it always looks wonderful – especially with a tan.

A white or light beige blazer or jacket. This can be worn over your existing skirts and trousers and with the T-shirts will give a cool summery look.

A pair of white cotton pants or jeans. (If budget permits, one white and one beige, as they do tend to live at the cleaners a lot.) These should be straight-legged, or if you have the figure for it lightly gathered over the hips and narrowing towards the ankle.

Three or four T-shirt tops in basic bright colours, e.g. orange, blue, turquoise, pink. (And by the way, wearing a T-shirt with a printed slogan on it is very old hat and sends

One of my favourite outfits is this all-in-one jump suit. It's great for parties and hot summer days.

you straight back to the Seventies. You are you. Don't advertize.)

A plain cotton or linen skirt in a bright colour. This should be knee length if your legs can take it, fairly form-fitting but not skin tight, and perhaps with a split at the side or back.

One cotton dirndl or peasant-type skirt in a printed or floral pattern. There are many beautiful and quite inexpensive skirts from India in the shops. I have collected several, some of which I have had for years – I drag them out of the cupboard each summer and they still look good.

A pair of khaki or white cotton or linen Bermuda shorts. These can be worn with the T-shirts or your other shirts, and may be worn either Bermuda length (as illustrated) or rolled up to make short shorts. You can also use your old flared jeans or trousers by cutting them off at thigh length. I don't advise shorts in the city – they are definitely for country or beach wear only.

A one-piece swimsuit or leotard. A leotard is terrific on the beach and much newer looking than a bikini. You can also exercise in it.

A bikini (if you've got the body for it).

A kanga. This is a large straight piece of printed cotton material which can be tied and draped around the body in a variety of ways. The prettiest ones come from Africa or Hawaii and can be bought relatively cheaply in many shops. If you cannot find one just buy the length of fabric you want and hem it yourself. This is invaluable for wearing over your bathing suit, either tied under the arms or at the waist or hips (see illustration), and is extremely versatile and attractive.

One pair of high-heeled white or beige sandals. The ones with stacked wooden heels are more practical than those of one colour because the heels don't show scuff marks.

One pair of flattish sandals or espadrilles.

Naturally if you are off on holiday you will need to add a light cotton sun dress or something that will do for the evening, and probably an extra bikini or two and a cotton 'boob tube'. But the list above should provide the basis to get you easily through the summer.

Two ways of wearing the kanga: left, as a bikini cover-up; right, as a beach dress which can double for a summer party or just being at home. An invaluable item for the summer wardrobe.

Tips for a new look

If you simply can't afford to buy a new wardrobe, here are some additions you can make to your present one that will give it a new look. I have specially chosen some of the current items and trends to watch.

Knit dresses are one of the most important new looks. You may choose a dress or two-piece in any variety of knits or patterns – flat, heavy sweater, silk or wool.

Fake fur is enjoying a new popularity now. It's an ecological, affordable and fun way to wear furs, from zebra to ocelot. And a fake fur coat is usually no more expensive than a cloth one.

A scarf in a vibrant colour – royal blue, magenta, fuchsia, purple – can brighten up any neutral outfit.

A classic belt in bright coloured suede – red, purple, tan – or a soft, crushable sash, also in bright suede.

A pair of straight-legged jeans, but in a stretch fabric.

A necklace of pearls or gold beads, uniform not graduated, about 2 feet long, and a cuff bracelet in sterling silver or gilt.

A leotard to wear with jeans and skirts or while exercising.

Earrings in silver or gold in a geometric shape that clip on the ear.

Gloves of any kind – wool, leather or suede.

A 'boob tube', sequined or in a glittery fabric, to wear with jeans or a skirt to make a stunningly sexy evening or disco look.

A track suit – one of the most comfortable, cosy and practical garments around in the shops now (sometimes called a jogging outfit). It looks terrifically coordinated, is superbly comfortable (infinitely more so than the ubiquitous blue jeans) and has, naturally, a rather sportive look.

Since my husband gave me one last Christmas I have practically lived in it, and it is now and will always be an indispensable part of my wardrobe.

How to look good in your clothes

It doesn't matter how expensive your clothes, or how much care you have taken choosing your wardrobe, if you do not know how to walk, sit and move well you will have no impact at all. So let's take a look at that old-fashioned word deportment.

Many women today don't know how to move gracefully, or even how to sit with any kind of attractiveness or ease. In my formative years mothers and grandmas placed a great deal of importance on posture and deportment. Unfortunately in the past two decades the emphasis has been concentrated more on 'doing your own thing' inwardly than in projecting an attractive outer image. Both of course are important, but one need not negate the other.

The habits you develop at the age of three or seven or ten will last a lifetime. If you sit and walk gracefully as a seven year old you will not slump at seventeen or seventy.

Changing your carriage is quite simple if you apply yourself positively to the project. Start by keeping the shoulders back and the spine straight. Feel as if an invisible wire is attached to the centre of your skull and is pulling you upward. Now hold in the stomach. When you hold it in, not only is it good for the muscles but it automatically makes your spine straighten and your shoulders come back. Don't sit with your legs spread apart unless you are wearing the most casual of jeans. Even then it's not a position which is conducive to good posture and is also fairly unattractive to look at.

Practise in front of a mirror walking, sitting, eating, drinking, even watching television, things that you do every day. How do you know how you look doing these activities if you've never seen yourself doing them?

As an actress I've had the opportunity to observe myself hundreds of different times on the screen. I have been able to correct some of the habits I didn't like about myself. For instance, as a teenager I used when nervous to rub my fingers and nails together in an unconscious gesture. Seeing this on the screen a few times I stopped myself doing it both in life and on the screen. Get your best friend, husband, mother, lover to observe you for a few days and check out your deportment flaws. Corrections can be easy. Remember the basics of all beauty are self-discipline and routine. And practice makes perfect!

Left: As our grandmothers looked in the Twenties, and as I appeared in The Last of Mrs Cheyney. *The Twenties is my favourite period: clothes were sleek, hard and stylish and very difficult to wear.*

Near right: Although I wore this outfit in the late Fifties it could all be worn today – proving that classic design needn't date.

Far right: I was mad about the mini, now having a 1980's renaissance.

Below: I loved the freedom of expression that emerged in dressing during the Seventies. For some time I adored the gypsy ethnic look and used to put everything on except the kitchen sink!

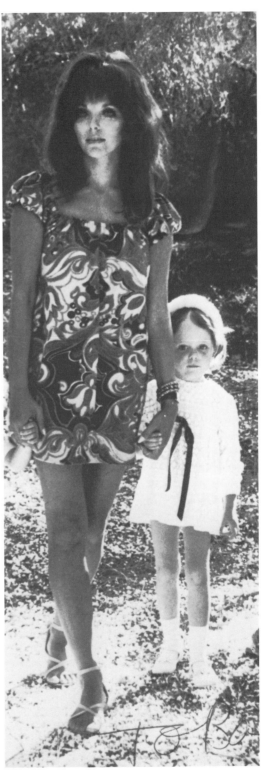

with Katyana, aged four days

Pregnancy

The first thing I did when I learned that I was pregnant with Tara, my first child, was to head for the fridge and start 'eating for two' – absolutely fatal! With the natural hormonal balance of the body altered, I found I had a gargantuan appetite for foods that I usually avoided – buns, crisps, cakes, fried food. I gained 10lb in as many weeks and burst out of my clothes before realizing that my self-indulgence was not doing me or my baby any good.

My doctor put me on the right track, making me cut down on calories and at the same time increase the vitamins and proteins I and the baby needed. He told me that the old wives' adage of eating for two was utter nonsense, and that one must increase the *quality* of what was consumed and not the quantity.

From then on my daily diet consisted of four or five glasses of milk – vital in pregnancy, as it is full of calcium which ensures excellent growth of the baby's bones and teeth – two servings of lean meat or liver or poultry a day, and at least three times a week a portion of fish. I had a large glass of fresh orange juice, preferably in the morning (the benefits of fresh juice far outweigh those of the tinned variety; canned fruit juice has many more calories, plus sugar, than the natural juice and it is bad for teeth, weight and health). I ate at least two large salads a day and as many fresh, lightly cooked or raw vegetables as I could to kill the hunger pangs – carrot and celery sticks and raw cauliflower blossoms filled the void between lunch and dinner.

Two eggs, two or three pieces of wholemeal bread and as much fruit as I wanted, and the cravings for ice cream, pickles, chips and sausage rolls soon abated.

So that was my basic diet – good for me and great for baby. On top of this, I bought a jar of calcium tablets which I crunched throughout the day. Most people thought that I was crazy to eat so much pure calcium but my theory is that calcium builds strong healthy teeth and bones. It seems to have paid off, for Tara, who is now seventeen, Sacha, fifteen, and Katyana, eight, have perfect teeth and have never had a filling or any dental problems. Since I spent half my life at the dentist as a child and growing adult, my 'prevention is better than cure' theory really does work. I increased my vitamin intake and took extra C and D, and also iron tablets.

I also cut out smoking completely, as I believe that women who smoke give birth to smaller babies with a tendency to respiratory infections and susceptibility to illness. Doctors now recommend that pregnant women give up smoking, but sixteen years ago they were not so concerned. When you inhale carbon monoxide, which is a poisonous gas, with your cigarette spare a thought for the baby in your womb, and if you cannot give up the ghastly weed at least try to cut down and *don't* inhale.

After paying all this attention to what went inside, I concentrated on what was best for the outside. Stretch marks . . . ugh ! So ugly ! 'The medals of pregnancy' – another old wives' tale I wasn't about to let pass without a struggle.

'There is nothing you can do to prevent stretch marks,' said my doctor sadly but definitively. 'But why do some women have them and some not ?' I argued. 'Luck, my dear – the luck of the draw. Just try not to put on too much weight.'

I decided that was baloney. Why should women have to suffer those nasty white tyre trails across their stomachs, thighs and behinds as their 'penalty' for giving birth ? I bought up every brand of cocoa butter on the market and religiously smothered myself in it three or four times a day. I also resolved to try and keep my weight down to the minimum. I continued to do my exercises, kept to the diet, and used the cocoa oil. Today, after sixteen years and three children, there is not a stretch mark on my body. For those who don't like the idea of cocoa butter, any rich emollient cream will do, so long as you use plenty of it.

The main thing to remember about being pregnant is that it is not a disease or an illness, it is one of the most natural things in the world, and most of the time you should be feeling in tip-top form. Generally it is during the first three months, before the world knows your secret, that you are most likely to suffer from some form of minor ailment. You may experience sickness in the morning or less commonly during the day, loss of appetite or more likely an increased need for food, and often excessive drowsiness at different times of the day. Each day when I was pregnant I walked at least a mile, trying to get to the relatively fresh air of the park rather than breathe in the noxious city smells and traffic exhausts. Whenever possible I would sit down and put my feet up; this takes the weight off the legs and feet which tend to swell up. While I was pregnant with Tara and Sacha, both times during the summer heat and humidity of New York, I found that my shoe size increased from $5\frac{1}{2}$ to 7! So I spent as much time as I could lying down with my legs and feet elevated, and at night I put a small pillow under my feet to keep them up. This helps the circulation and also prevents varicose veins, an unfortunate side-effect of pregnancy, often the result of being on your feet too much and of excessive weight gain.

Every morning I did about five minutes of exercises – mostly bending and stretching, nothing too strenuous for the first three months or the last two, but for the four months in between I was quite energetic and even went to the occasional disco.

With Katyana, my youngest child, I was much more stringent with myself as far as diet and exercise were concerned. My doctor decided that I should not gain more than 18lb, because this was my third child and the muscles had already been stretched by the two previous pregnancies. The chances of getting my figure back would be lessened by excessive weight gain. I obediently gained exactly 18lb. I was back in my normal clothes within nine days of Katy's birth, and feeling terrific. I also worked while I was six months pregnant, and since I did not tell anyone and gained little weight I was able to get away with it. I made a commercial for margarine in which I was supposed to look exceedingly glamorous, and floated around in a flowing silk shirt trying desperately to hold in my stomach.

With a little care, discipline, common sense and will power there is no reason to believe that you should not be back to your normal weight and condition within a very few weeks after your baby is born.

Whatever discomfort or difficulty you experienced during pregnancy or labour, it is a cliché but true that all is forgotten the moment you glimpse that tiny creased baby face that is yours and your own achievement. There is no more exciting or rewarding feeling in the world than the joy of creating a new human being, and however experienced a veteran you may be, you cannot fail to be thrilled by each new experience of giving birth.

Tips for ladies-in-waiting

You should always try to put by at least an hour for a nap or a rest in the afternoon, especially in the first and last months. Pregnancy does put extra stress on all your organs, including your heart which increases its blood flow by 40 per cent, and it is wise to pamper yourself.

A healthy mother usually has a healthy baby, so keep yourself in *peak* condition.

Large meals are hard to digest, so it is advisable to have four or five small meals a day, rather than two or three heavy ones.

Avoid coffee, tea, fizzy drinks and *all* drugs and patent medicines. Coffee and tea stimulate your nervous system and brain, and may keep you tossing and turning at night. Since you could have sleep problems in the last few weeks anyway, due to discomfort of the large bulge, it is better for you and the baby if you avoid stimulants. Drink warm milk and honey or hot lemon and honey; after a relaxing bath they are excellent sleep inducers.

If you find in the last few weeks that it is very difficult to find a comfortable position in which to sleep, turn on your side and place a baby pillow or small folded towel under your tummy. When sitting for long periods put a cushion in the small of your back.

Within twenty-four hours of the birth you should start doing *gentle* leg raises in your bed to tighten up the abdominal muscles. (Check with your doctor first.)

Wear a bra all the time — you'll probably have to get a larger size shortly after you discover you are pregnant. It's especially important to wear one when in bed.

with Katyana at six

Beauty Care for Children

A disciplined beauty routine, started young, is the basis for lifelong good looks.

Skin that is cleaned every day, nourished and protected will look much better at thirty, forty and fifty years than skin that has been neglected. Correct nutrition is the best investment you can make for your child's future.

When should a young girl start a regular beauty routine? Usually her body tells her. At the onset of puberty (nine to twelve years), hormones become active in ways that they have not been before. This results in a change in the skin. It may lose its childlike softness and smoothness, becoming slightly coarser, and break-out problems – blackheads or spots – may suddenly start.

Because of the activity of the oil glands at puberty, most teenagers tend to have slightly oily skin. As they get older their skin will usually become drier. Some teenagers however have to fight dry skin caused by their environment, and may have a combination skin. This necessitates two different types of treatment for the different areas of their skin. Usually the centre part of the face, a sort of triangle including nose, side of cheeks and chin, will be oily. This should be washed with one of the soaps on the market specially created for this problem. If the rest of the face is dry, it should be treated as described in the chapter on skin care (see page 61).

Teenagers should always be aware of the possibility of having to change their beauty routines, because skin changes constantly. As a girl becomes older her skin becomes drier, and requires extra care. Skin may break out around the time of her period, and she may need to take more care with it then. Skin exposed to sun and cold needs special treatment.

Ideally, a regular skin care programme should be started as early as two or three. At this age, a little girl should form the habit of washing her face regularly and using light baby products. By fourteen or fifteen she will probably need a special soap or lotion to cleanse her face, and may start wearing a light foundation to protect it during the day. She should also occasionally apply a moisturizer at night to combat dryness. By the age of fifteen or sixteen a girl should have developed a regular skin care programme, and should be protecting her skin by using moisturizers and other preparations.

No one is ever too young or too old to begin a regular skin care programme. My mother introduced me to cold cream soon after I entered my teens. Since she herself had fine dry skin which I inherited, she believed, as I do, in an early start. I began taking care of my own children's skin when they were extremely young. Now I give Katyana, who is eight, a 'beauty treatment' about once every ten days or so. We pretend she's going to the beauty parlour and make a game of it, which is fun for her and for me too!

Assuming that it is never too young to begin, here is a simple regime for your daughter of say four to twelve years old, that will lay the foundation for healthy habits and lovely skin and hair for the rest of her life.

Bath-time

Always use baby soap or a mild non-alkaline soap on your little girl's skin. Even though her skin has lots of natural moisture, the use of harsh soaps and detergents can start drying it up too early.

Don't use bubble baths supposedly specially made for children: they are much too harsh. If she likes to play in a bubble bath, make certain it is a mild one, as those made for adults usually are.

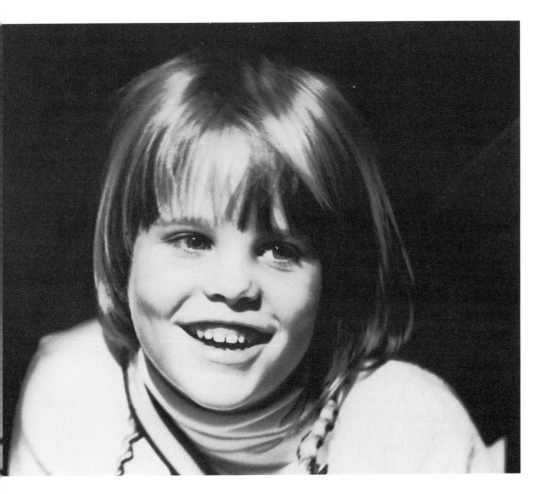

Katyana at five, preparing to be a beautiful lady and loving it.

It isn't necessary to bath every single night, unless she has been playing in the mud or has become particularly dirty. Every other night is quite often enough – too much bathing tends to lose precious moisture even at this age.

Once a week put a capful of baby oil in the bath. It softens the skin.

Always make her wash her face *first* in the bath before her body, or preferably wash face before in the wash basin. Have a separate face cloth for the face and for the body.

After patting the skin dry, apply lotion or some other similar cream on legs and arms, especially knees which have a tendency to get chapped in winter.

Dust baby talcum powder on the rest of the body to finish.

Once or twice a week use a gentle baby lotion on her face.

Hair

Children's hair should be washed a maximum of twice a week, preferably only once. Their hair is more delicate than that of adults, and needs extremely gentle care. Too much shampooing strips hair of its natural oils.

After being washed, the hair should be dried with a towel and left to dry naturally if possible. Try to avoid using the blow drier until she's older.

Hair should be trimmed regularly to avoid split ends. If your daughter wears plaits, split ends are more liable to occur. If she must wear plaits or a pony tail to school, give her hair a rest at weekends and let it hang loose. *Never* use ordinary rubber bands for pony tails and braids: they break the hair. Always use ribbon, twine or coated rubber bands from the haberdashery department.

If your child has a fringe, make sure you cut it regularly so it doesn't fall into her eyes all the time, which can be a distraction and is bad for the eyes. If she has extremely fine hair keep it cut as short as possible. My daughter Tara was practically bald until she was eighteen months old, and when her hair began growing it was baby-fine and thin. I kept cutting it extremely short until she was about nine or ten and still kept it reasonably short even then. Now at sixteen she has the most beautiful, luxuriant, full head of hair, and she takes excellent care of it.

Avoid curling, crimping and doing fancy things with children's hair. It is naturally beautiful, and looks best clean, brushed and left well alone.

Teeth

Care of the teeth is terribly important. It should be started as early as possible: buy your baby a soft bristle toothbrush when the first tooth appears, and make it a game to polish the one little tooth every night. Don't use hard nylon brushes as they will scratch the enamel. Brush teeth after breakfast, and before bedtime *always*.

With Tara at the age of nine. Her hair had been kept very short to ensure its future strength and thickness.

There is still controversy over the benefits of toothpaste with added fluoride. I have always used fluoride toothpastes for my three children, however, and now at the ages of seventeen, fifteen and eight they have no fillings, decayed teeth or cavities yet.

Diet

Young children

For good healthy teeth, bones and skin it is essential that children eat each day at least one portion of the following: milk, dark green vegetables, wholegrain bread or cereal, citrus fruit, eggs, poultry or fish. Red meat is not necessary more than twice a week.

Avoid as far as possible sticky sweets and toffees, buns, biscuits, crisps, cakes and jam. It is virtually impossible to eliminate all of these from your children's diet. Seeing their friends eat them, seeing them 'sold' on television, makes them feel deprived if they can't have them too. But it is absolutely worth the effort to try. Substitute cheese, peanut butter, apples, tangerines, nuts, raisins, fruit, jelly made without sugar, raw celery, carrot sticks, or whole-wheat toast with honey if your child needs a snack.

Avoid like the plague all those sweet fizzy drinks; they are the ultimate teeth rotters as well as being slightly addictive. We do not allow them in our house. Apple juice, blackcurrant juice, fresh orange juice, milk, milk shakes made with non-additive colouring, and orange and lemon squash are infinitely better. Young children should not be given tea, coffee, spicy food or pepper, and they should take as little salt as possible. (I have never put salt in my children's vegetables nor on the table, and since you don't miss what you have not had, mine don't ask for it.)

It is essential to remember that a fat child almost certainly becomes a fat adult, so if your little one is a touch overweight, start *now* cutting down the calories. Obesity is becoming more and more prevalent, especially in America, Canada and Western Europe. This is mainly due to people eating too much of the wrong food, which I'm afraid is the 'convenience' food so attractively and widely advertized.

When you give your children lamb or pork chops or a steak, always cut off all the fat – then they will get into the habit of doing that too. Always try to use vegetable oil instead of lard, bacon grease, dripping or animal fat. Cut out all those pre-packaged custards and desserts in favour of yoghurt and fresh fruit and cheese.

Finally, your child will benefit from a multi-vitamin pill every morning and, in the winter especially, one or two natural Vitamin C tablets. Children do not need to take any other vitamin pills if their diet is adequate.

Teenagers

How many young girls know how to eat properly? Not too many, in my opinion. Breakfast is often forgotten, lunch skimped; dinner may be a greasy hamburger or pizza or chips. In between, gaps are filled by starchy snacks and soft drinks whose nutritional value is zero. All this, of course, adds greatly to the adolescent worries that may already exist: weight problems, skin problems and lack of energy. You owe it to your daughters (and sons too) to get them into healthy eating habits from an early age – this way they may avoid the worst of the teenage pitfalls.

My children Tara, Katyana and Sacha. I try to make sure they follow my concepts of correct nutrition as much as one can make a child or teenager do so. So far it has paid off!

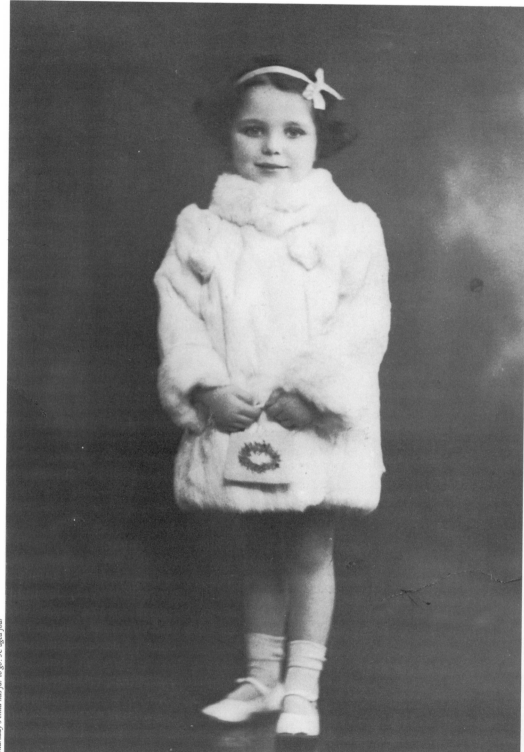

facing the future

If antiques and fine wine improve with age, why shouldn't women do the same? Never before has it been possible for women to stay looking younger longer. No longer are most of us worn out and exhausted by childbirth and housework. We know much today about correct nutrition and physical fitness, and the vast cosmetic industry is geared to our needs, constantly perfecting new products for preserving and maintaining the elasticity and suppleness of our skins. Although we cannot stop the inevitable ageing process, it is now possible to slow it down considerably.

Today there is a tremendous difference between biological and chronological age. Two women of identical years can look totally different ages depending on the way they have maintained themselves. I have seen thirty-five year olds who look twenty-five, and thirty-five year olds who look forty-five. A lot of it has to do with the luck of the draw as far as parents go, of course: if Mum or Dad look good at sixty, the chances are you will too. (My grandparents lived to be ninety and my father is seventy-seven and looks great, so I'm crossing my fingers!) But if your parents are fit and vigorous it is highly probable that, by accident or design, they have formed good health habits throughout their lifetime.

Thirty years ago a woman was finished by the age of forty. Today forty is just the beginning, and with the possibility of at least another thirty-five years of active life to enjoy, it's no wonder that there are so many fabulous over-forties around.

Experience is something to be proud of, not to hide. If you think of the top film actresses of today, it is hard to come up with many who are actually *under* forty. Virtually none are under thirty-five – unthinkable twenty-five years ago, when a woman's value was rated by her lack of years. As an example, I was voted in 1979 by a poll of young men between the ages of twenty-five and thirty-five in the UK their most desirable woman in the world. Heady stuff, even for a twenty year old. I was flattered not only for myself, but because some of the other women in the poll were closer to forty than thirty.

Age – although a touchy subject for many because of long-held taboos – should no longer be considered a barrier to a full life. There is for some reason (in Western society only) an incredible snobbery about age – an attitude towards middle and old age that it is something to hide, to be ashamed of. In the United States women and men too now flock to face-lift parlours in a desperate attempt to remain young and acceptable. But the average age of the whole population is now about thirty; by the year 2000 it will be forty. So since we are all living longer we must not let up but live life to the full and rid ourselves of old-fashioned concepts about ageing. Just remember, you're not only getting older, you're getting better!

Each age has its own advantages. Wisdom, tolerance and humour are gained as one progresses through life, in exchange for some loss of freshness and innocence. Of course many of us dread old age because we feel death cannot then be too far away; but we are programmed to die from the day we are born, just as we are programmed to age. If our *attitudes* are right, our life should only become richer as time passes.

Basic dress sense, acquired in the teens and twenties, will blossom with experience. Particularly in terms of hair, make-up and clothes, less is more and simplicity is all. There are few things more pitiful than a woman in her fifties emulating a twenty year old's clothes, attitude and make-up. On the other hand a woman of that age who is beautifully groomed and dressed with taste, who has taken

174

care of herself, can be truly beautiful. The 'mutton done up as lamb' syndrome is to be avoided at all cost.

The proof of the pudding is in the eating, so they say. And the proof that correct diet and taking care of yourself on a regular basis pays off in later years is proved by the examples on the following pages of beautiful, attractive, glowing women from every age group. Although I don't know them all personally I'm quite sure they don't live on a diet of cream buns and spaghetti!

To me the greatest example of a wonderful looking woman, no matter what her age, is The Queen Mother. Glamorous, stately, warm, humorous, she found her own style both in dress and attitude years ago and stuck to it. She epitomizes all the warm qualities of a relaxed 'glamorous granny', with the dedication to duty of someone who has spent her life in the service of the public and enjoyed it.

Our much loved and elegant Queen Mother, now in her eighties.

Other beauties in the over-seventies age group include Lady Diana Cooper, Barbara Cartland, Gloria Swanson, Cathleen Nesbitt and Greta Garbo. All have definite approaches to health, style and life, and seem to be still extremely vigorous and healthy.

Here are some examples of good looking women in their sixties. Dame Margot Fonteyn is simply breathtaking. Her body is that of a young girl, and her movements always memorable. Obviously the rigorous schedule of practice, exercise and rehearsals to which she has adhered all her life has a great deal to do with her wonderful physique. The actress Evelyn Laye is another woman who created her own style years ago, found it suited her and adapted it to modern trends. Ingrid Bergman is a supreme example of beauty that has matured into the kind of loveliness that only utter contentment and calmness can bring. Without make-up, in simple clothes and not particularly slender, she is without doubt a truly glowing beauty.

The legendary beauty Lady Diana Cooper.

Some other super sixties include Dinah Shore, Deborah Kerr, Ann Miller, Lena Horne and Dame Alicia Markova.

In the fifties age group there are dozens of ladies who look sensational and have zip, bazaaz, oomph, sex appeal – whatever you call it. Twenty years ago one wouldn't believe that women of fifty could look so young and vital, but with ladies like Lauren Bacall, Grace Kelly, Jackie Onassis, Audrey Hepburn, Cyd Charisse, Gina Lollabrigida, Katie Boyle and Janet Leigh, to name but a few, it's no wonder women go green with envy.

And then there are the mere striplings – the forty-pluses, many of whom could pass for twenty-eight at any time. These particular ladies seem to have done more than any others to alter attitudes about the beauty of a woman being dependent on whether or not she is 'young'. Sophia Loren, Brigitte Bardot, Jane Fonda, Angie Dickinson, Edna O'Brien, Raquel Welch, Ursula Andress, Diana Rigg, Julie Christie, Claudia Cardinale, Tessa Kennedy, Ali McGraw and many others are all a living testament that getting older is getting better. I am certain that all of them take particular care of their health and diet (none of them are in any way overweight), of their bodies and looks, and are women who realize that true beauty depends on a good foundation. If you follow my advice on these subjects in the book, it can pay off for you too. You could identify with Sophia Loren who, when complimented on the fact that she was now more beautiful than twenty years ago, replied with a smile 'I know'.

You get the face and body you deserve after a certain age. If you allow bitterness and discontent to be your lot, it's going to be pretty difficult to look sexy, attractive and glowing. Self-confidence and just that plain old 'glad to be on the planet earth' feeling is more beneficial than any cosmetic and beauty product, and it *must* come first. All the cosmetics in the world cannot hide hardness, coldness and emptiness inside. That is why I think it is vitally important for every woman to do her own thing. It doesn't matter if her 'thing' is pursuing a flourishing career, or working eight hours a day in a factory, or staying at home and watching the children grow up. It is only by self-fulfilment and the feeling that you and only you are the mistress of your destiny that you can ever begin to achieve the inner peace and strength from which all true beauty stems.

Giant steps have been taken in the last fifteen years. The Pill, Women's Lib, the economic necessity for a two-earning family and the growing acceptance of woman's vital role in society have all contributed. It is not necessary to do what the early Women's Libbers of the Sixties did, disowning their overt feminine attributes in favour of burning their bras, scrubbing their faces and eschewing pretty clothes. Men didn't want to know about such dominant, aggressive women, and who can blame them. Gradually since then has come the renaissance of the attractive feminine woman, who accepts and enjoys her femininity.

The greatest advantage we have as women is our femininity, and we should *use* it – not as a weapon but as an asset. We can of course be aggressive and domineering at times, but we must never lose sight of our own persona, attractiveness and natural gentleness. Men shave, use cologne and have their hair cut, and are not considered frivolous for doing so. If we as women can give pleasure to other people by our appearance, who is to say we are not serious?

As women become stronger and more independent, they will be able more and more to do what they feel is right for them and not what society dictates. Since young men today were not raised with the old-fashioned attitudes of male dominance, but grew up with a new awareness of the equality of the male–female role, they don't feel their masculinity is threatened by being asked to cook, clean, sew and help with the baby too. By the same token women can fix a fuse, change a tyre, go to work and do many other things once purely the prerogative of the 'dominant' male.

The whole male–female relationship is entering a most interesting and delicate phase now. But until the modern world recognizes the rights of *all* women to have their own identity – be it as mother, wife, career woman, or all three – and women can be accepted totally as they really are without having to conform to the patterns forced on them, we are still far from a non-sexist and equal society.

Meanwhile, ladies, don't let them get you down because you want to be beautiful. As the song says, 'Enjoy being a girl!' You cannot live your life through others: you must live for yourself. This may sound selfish, but if others are to like and love you it is imperative that you truly like and love yourself.

Index

Picture Acknowledgements

The author and publishers wish to thank the following for permission to reproduce their photographs:

John Adriaan 15. Courtesy Elizabeth Arden Ltd 62, 64, 101 top right/bottom, 116 top/bottom, 117 top/bottom, 127 top, 128 top. Brian Aris/Scope Features 25–29, 56, 66–67, 71, 86, 105–107, 130, 151, 164, 171. Associated Newspapers 175, 176. Author's Collection 89 bottom, 156 top, 157 right, 168, 172. Tony Boas 115. Bookings/Photograph Kenneth Deiber 101 top left. Courtesy Boots No. 7 109 top. Brent-Walker Films opp. 1. 20th Century Fox 157 left. Terence Donovan 112. John French 89 top. Kent Gavin/Daily Mirror 10, 20–24, 153. Peter Gowland 100. Ron Kass 167. Herman Leonard 68, 69, 70, 140. Courtesy Max Factor 65 top, 72. Courtesy L'Oreal 110 bottom. Rank Organisation 156 bottom. Courtesy Revlon 108 top/bottom, 109 bottom, 126, 127 bottom, 128 bottom, 129. Eddie Sanderson/Scope Features 30, 36, 80. David Steen/Scope Features 65 bottom, 158. Vivienne Ventura 32. Courtesy Wella Hair Cosmetics 110 top, 111 top/bottom.

While every effort has been made to trace the copyright owners, the publishers wish to state that if anyone has been overlooked they will be pleased to make amends at the earliest opportunity.